TERMINAL VELOCITY

Investigating Forces and Motion in Our Universe

P9-DNI-381

The
JASON
Project™

SEA RESEARCH FOUNDATION   NATIONAL GEOGRAPHIC

The JASON Project and its Immersion Learning program inspire and educate kids everywhere through real science and exploration. JASON is an independent 501(c)(3) operated in partnership with National Geographic Society, Sea Research Foundation, Inc., and the National Oceanic and Atmospheric Administration (NOAA). JASON focuses on classroom-based curriculum experiences. Immersion delivers complementary out-of-school science programs for use in after school, mentoring and camp programs.

Visit *www.jason.org* to learn more about The JASON Project, or email us at *info@jason.org*.

Cover Design: Ryan Kincade, The JASON Project

Cover Images

Main cover and title page: ernest/flickr

Front cover thumbnails: Peter Haydock, The JASON Project.

Back cover thumbnails: (top left) Teacher Argonaut Kelly Stewart. Photo by Peter Haydock, The JASON Project; (middle right) Student Argonaut Aubrey Gonzalez. Photo by Peter Haydock, The JASON Project; (bottom left) Student Argonaut Marcelo Ancira. Photo by Peter Haydock, The JASON Project; (bottom right) Steamroller Photo by rejar/flickr; Crash Photo by The Insurance Institute for Highway Safety.

Published by The JASON Project.

© 2011 The JASON Project. All rights reserved. No part of this publication may be kept in any information storage or retrieval system, transmitted, or reproduced in any form or by any means, electronic or mechanical, without the prior written consent of The JASON Project.

Requests for permission to copy or distribute any part of this work should be addressed to

The JASON Project
Permissions Requests
44983 Knoll Square
Ashburn, VA 20147

Phone: 888-527-6600
Fax: 877-370-8988

ISBN 978-1-935211-41-9

Printed in the United States of America
by the Courier Companies, Inc.

10 9 8 7 6 5 4 3 2 1

National Geographic and the Yellow Border are trademarks of the National Geographic Society.

Contents

2 Getting Started with *Terminal Velocity*

4 Your Tour of the *JASON* Expedition Center

6 Terminal Velocity Overview

Expeditions

10 **Expedition 1:** *Critical Measurements—The Quest for Exactness*
Stage 1: Communicating with Measurements
Stage 2: Derived Units
Stage 3: Accuracy and Precision

Field Assignment: Stringing Along

Lab: Measuring With Tools
Lab: Measuring Mysteries
Lab: Targeting, Accuracy, and Precision

36 **Expedition 2:** *A Universe of Motion—Motion, Velocity, and Momentum*
Stage 1: On the Move

Stage 2: Speeding Up, Slowing Down, and Spinning Around
Stage 3: When Paths Collide
Field Assignment: Performing Crash Tests

Lab: Calculating Speed and Determining Velocity
Lab: Acceleration

Lab: Momentum
Math Connections

70 **Expedition 3:** *Fundamental Forces—Forces and the Laws of Motion*
Stage 1: The Nature of Forces and Inertia
Stage 2: The Nature of Forces and Acceleration
Stage 3: Dynamic Fluids
Field Assignment: To Infinity and Beyond

Lab: A Touch of Force
Lab: It's a Blast
Lab: Cartesian Diver
Math Connections

98 **Expedition 4:** *Make It Work—Work, Power, and Machines*
Stage 1: Let's Get to Work!
Stage 2: There Has to be an Easier Way
Stage 3: Man versus Machine
Field Assignment: Man vs. Machine

Lab: Work
Lab: Simple Machines
Lab: Complex Machines
Math Connections

Connections

34 History
Underwater Cables

68 Sports and Technology
Home Run

96 Arts and Entertainment
Physics of the Circus

130 History
The Renaissance Man Leonardo da Vinci

132 Machines on Expedition
Remotely Operated Vehicles

Features

136 The JASON Project Argonaut Program

138 Forces and Motion Tools

139 Glossary

Sebastian Batardy/flickr

Getting Started with *Terminal Velocity*

Developed in collaboration with our partners at National Geographic, NOAA, the National Institute of Standards and Technology, the Insurance Institute for Highway Safety, and other leading organizations, *Terminal Velocity* is built on an Expedition framework to capture the energy and excitement of authentic exploration and discovery. The curriculum consists of four captivating Expeditions that provide the real-world challenges, scientific background knowledge, and tools to help you complete each expedition goal.

Let's take a closer look at the parts of each Expedition!

Expedition Goals

Each Expedition starts with a list of objectives that you will find on this opening page.

Join The Team

Your Expedition begins with an invitation to the join the Host Researcher and Argonaut team. You will work side-by-side with this team as they guide you through your study of physics.

Video and Online Resources

You will also see icons directing you to the Host Researcher Video, where you will get to know more about the Expedition team leader. Watch for these icons and others. They indicate when you will find multimedia resources online in the **JASON Expedition Center**.

Introduction Article

Once you have your goals and have met the team, each new Expedition will introduce you to a day in the life of the Host Researcher and the unique work that brings this scientist face-to-face with physics concepts.

Expedition Briefing Video

See these adventures come alive in every Expedition Briefing Video, which gives an action-packed introduction to the Expedition goals and key science concepts.

Expedition Briefing Articles

Gather all of your background information and clues through a series of Expedition Briefing Articles that guide you through the science of physics, so that you can complete your Expedition goals.

Full-color graphics enhance the description and explanation of essential science concepts, so you can clearly see the ideas presented in the briefings.

Fast Facts and Examples

You will find interesting things you have never thought of before in Fast Facts and Examples.

Researcher Tools

Check out the amazing tools that researchers use during their explorations in the field.

Our Ocean Planet

Check out examples of how physics concepts can be applied to studying the ocean.

Team Highlights

Get an up-close view of the investigations that our Host Researchers and Argonauts conducted during their field work for *Terminal Velocity*.

Expedition Labs

Put your knowledge to work with several hands-on labs in each Expedition. The labs provide opportunities to practice and refine the skills you need in order to complete your expedition goals. In these labs, you will build tools, conduct investigations, collect data, and describe your observations and conclusions in your JASON Journal.

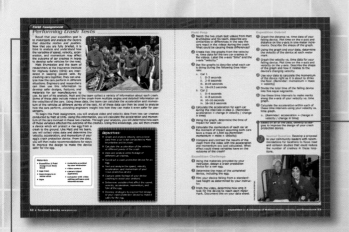

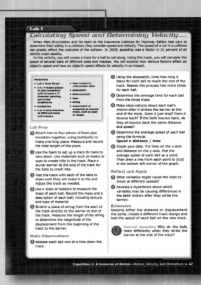

Connections

Learn to look for and find the amazing connections between science concepts and other things that you experience in the world around you. *Connections* highlight thought-provoking links that you can explore between science and human culture, history, geography, math, literature, strange phenomena, and other interesting topics.

Field Assignment

Field Assignments at the conclusion of each Expedition give you the opportunity to put your new science skills and ideas to work in the field. To complete your Expedition goals, you will need to accomplish the goals set out in a Expedition Challenge, and then provide an analysis during your Expedition Debrief.

Argonaut Videos, Journals, and Photo Galleries

Join the Argo team as they conduct their field work for selected expeditions around the country. Log into the **JASON Expedition Center** to read the Argonaut journals and take a look at the photo galleries documenting their field experiences.

Your Tour of the JASON Expedition Center

The **JASON Expedition Center** is your online hub for *Terminal Velocity* content and resources and for the Argonaut community. Your JASON experience will come to life through interactive games, digital labs, video segments, your own JASON Journals, and other community resources and tools that support the Expeditions in this book.

Create Your Own Free Student Account

If your teacher has made an account for you, simply log into the **JASON Expedition Center.** Otherwise, follow these simple steps below to create your own account.

1. Go to *www.jason.org*.
2. Look for the **JASON Expedition Center** in the upper right corner.
3. Click **Register**.
4. Choose "Student" as your role –*OR*– if your teacher provided you with a class-room code, click the link to enter it now.
5. Enter a username and select a password for your account that you can easily remember.

The JASON Expedition Center Home Page

Welcome to your **JASON Expedition Center** home page. From here you can quickly access all the wonderful JASON tools and resources as you begin your expedition. Take a moment to read the latest JASON news, try a search of the Digital Library, or jump right into *Terminal Velocity* on the Web.

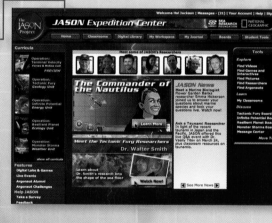

Your Resources and Tools

Powerful online tools are always at your fingertips. Use the *Digital Library* to find any JASON resource quickly and easily. Save and organize your favorites in *My Workspace*. View assignments and community updates in your *Classrooms* menu. These resources and more are always accessible through the *Tools* menu at the top of the **JASON Expedition Center** page.

My Journals and Other Community Tools

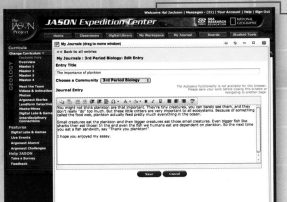

Your student account in the **JASON Expedition Center** includes an online JASON Journal that allows you to take notes, write about what you have learned, and respond to journal questions during the Expeditions. Other Community Tools include a moderated message board, classroom home pages, and tools to communicate with JASON researchers about their ongoing work in the field.

Online Version of Terminal Velocity

This entire student edition book is also available to you on-line, for easy access anytime, anywhere. You can view any page from any Expedition.

Team Info, Videos, and Photo Galleries

Learn more about the Host Researchers and the Argonauts from their biographies and journals. Video segments feature the Expedition teams in action. Photo galleries provide additional views of the researchers and Argonauts at work, as well as stunning collections of more physics concepts in our world.

Peter Haydock/The JASON Project

Peter Haydock/The JASON Project

Interactive Games

Visit the JASON Expedition Center for digital labs and games. Explore the oceans as you apply your knowledge of forces and motion. Navigate ships and ROVs through exciting scenarios around the world.

Live Events

Communicate with great explorers through great events. JASON researchers work on the cutting-edge of science and are eager to share their stories of discovery and inspiration with students around the world.

Your Expedition begins at *www.jason.org*

TERMINAL VELOCITY

Investigating Forces and Motion in Our Universe

Visualizing Forces and Motion

Birds soar through the air, while apples fall from the trees. A ship made of steel floats on the water while a pebble immediately sinks. Why? How can we make sense of the forces and motion we observe every day? Why is it that some objects move while others lie motionless? Fascination with forces and motion can be traced back to early scientists whose curiosity led them to experiment and explore how our physical world works.

While scientists have discovered much about forces and motion over the course of time, curiosity about our universe continues today. And today's scientists are applying what scientists of the past learned, in new and interesting ways, leading to new discoveries and advancements in the fields of engineering, astronomy, rocketry, and medicine. Each new discovery provides us with more and more to explore.

Models

In their quest to discover more about the universe, scientists use models as a way to visualize and test their hypotheses. A **model** is any representation of an object or event used to explain the natural world. Models make it easier for us to see extremely small or large objects. They can also capture motion that is too slow or fast for us to observe. Some models even give us insight into objects not yet in existence.

Some models are actual physical representations of an object or system. You have probably built a model, such as a house made from building blocks or a model airplane. Scientists build models as well. They can use the models to test what would happen to the object the model represents under different conditions. Testing a new plane wing on a two-meter long model plane is much less expensive and time-consuming than testing it on a real plane.

IIHS

NASA

Maps, globes, and blueprints are also examples of models. By looking at a map of your state or the blueprint of a new house, you can visualize what the actual state or house looks like even though you can't see it. Some models can also show you how and why objects move. You can visualize the orbit of the moon around Earth or the motion of the entire solar system using a physical model or even a 3-D model developed on a computer.

Computers can help scientists use mathematical formulas and tables to quickly model different scenarios. Changes to a model can be made much more easily using a computer than by physically building a new model to test different sizes, shapes, or speeds. Computer models are relatively new and have only been available to scientists in recent years. Computer models have made it possible for Host Researcher Dan Sawyer and other engineers at NIST to make measurements and measuring tools faster, better, and more cost effective.

Some models are little more than ideas in a scientist's head, yet they can be just as useful in understanding how the world around us works. For example, the Laws of Motion developed by Sir Isaac Newton are models that explain the relationships among mass, acceleration, and forces. You cannot pick up Newton's Laws of Motion and examine them like a globe, but you can use them to describe and predict a variety of motions and forces around you.

Models often save time, money, and even lives. Just ask Host Researcher Matt Brumbelow and his team at IIHS. They use crash dummies and are able to visually see the effectiveness of seat belts, bumpers, and air bags as tools to save lives in automobile crashes. By connecting these dummies to computers, they can easily model changes in variables such as speed, acceleration, mass, and force. Idea models, such as Newton's Laws of Motion, provide the mathematical formulas that the computers use to model these changes.

Models can change as new information and technology are discovered. By using models to test predictions, scientists will continue to make new discoveries and advancements in the fields of engineering, astronomy, rocketry, and medicine. The timeline on the following pages give you a brief picture of some scientists who used models to shape our current knowledge about forces and motion.

Every Picture Tells a Story

When a scientist or engineer collects data, the information is generally first put into a data table. This "raw" data format can be difficult to interpret. Organizing the data is an important part of communicating the results of an experiment. Scientists use graphs to turn these raw numbers into a visual representation. It is much easier to see trends and draw conclusions about data when they are shown in a graph. Common graphs include line, bar, and circle graphs.

There are guidelines for each type of graph that scientists and engineers use. These guidelines allow them to effectively communicate their findings to others. Each of the engineers and scientists in *Terminal Velocity* and the other JASON Project curricula use graphs to help them understand and communicate their data.

When representing data sets with graphs, scientists must first understand what kind of data they have. This allows them to choose which kind of graph to create from that data. Do the data show the relationship between two measurements or do the data show subsets from a whole data set? Each of the three basic types of graphs—line, bar, and circle—have their own best use.

Graphs tell a visual story about the data that is collected during experimentation. Learning to draw graphs correctly is a necessary skill for scientists and students like you. Data must be accurately collected and correctly plotted if the graph is to be meaningful.

Scale is important when creating graphs. The numbers on the x- and y-axes make up the scale. These numbers can start at zero, or another number can be used. They usually end at a number near the highest value of the data being graphed. These numbers should be evenly distributed—constant in value and distance—in order to create a graph that accurately represents the data. The scale on the x-axis and on the y-axis do not have to be the same.

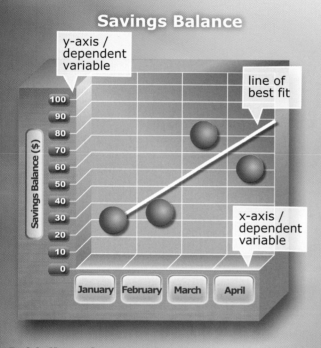

Savings Balance

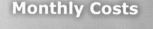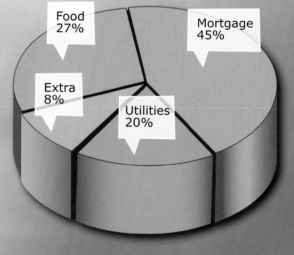

Monthly Costs

Guidelines for Creating a Line Graph

Many scientific graphs are line graphs. A line graph represents data using points. A line graph starts with data that has at least two numbers associated with each data point. The points show the relationship between two experimental variables. The independent, or manipulated variable, is plotted on the horizontal x-axis. The dependent, or responding, variable is plotted on the vertical y-axis.

Choose a line graph graph if you have at least two related number sets to present. Examples: time and temperature, time and distance, and time and population.

- Place the independent variable on the x-axis (horizontal).
- Place the dependent variable on the y-axis (vertical).
- Determine the scale for your graph.
- Place your data points on the graph and then draw a best fit line. Do not connect the data points unless you are drawing a mathematical equation or know every data point to make a line. Label your scale and indicate major lines within the graph. Make sure to title to your graph.

Guidelines for Creating a Circle Graph

A circle or pie graph represents groups of data as parts of a whole. The data are divided into fractions that look like the pieces of a pie. Colors are used with a key to explain what each fraction represents. For example, fractions might represent the number of different types of cars on the road, or the number of types of animals in an ecosystem.

Choose a circle graph if you need to represent parts of a whole.

- Label all components of your circle graph.
- Add a title and a legend.
- Use a key to explain what each color represents.
- Each wedge in a circle graph should be labeled with the data description and its relative (a percentage) or absolute value. Fill each wedge with a different color or texture fill.

Average Speed of Drivers by Age

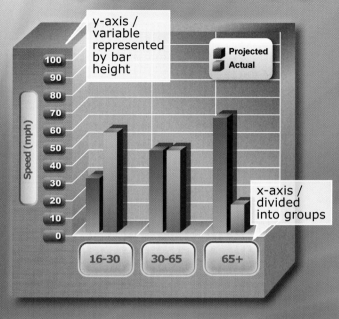

y-axis / variable represented by bar height

Speed (mph)

■ Projected
■ Actual

x-axis / divided into groups

16-30 30-65 65+

tm tm/flickr

Impact on Life Expectancy
(French Fries versus Apples)

Direct linear   Inverse linear

Life Expectancy   Life Expectancy

Fruits and Vegetables Consumed (g/day)   French Fries Eaten per day

Life Expectancy   Life Expectancy

Fruits and Vegetables Consumed (g/day)   French Fries Eaten per day

Direct nonlinear   Inverse nonlinear

Guidelines for Creating a Bar Graph

Bar graphs use vertical or horizontal bars to show the relationship between variables. The data can be represented in numbers or words. The length of the bar is a visual indication of the value of the variable. Histograms are a special type of bar graph where the data is shown in numerical order.

Bar graphs are often used to represent data sets. Simple bar graphs represent one independent and one dependent variable. However, bar graphs can be used to represent more complex data, such as comparing the same types of data from more than one data series. In these cases, the bar graph shows two or more independent variables and one dependent variable. For example, a bar graph could be used to represent the number of specific types of cars on the road in various locations, or the numbers of types of animals found in several different countries.

Choose a bar graph if you want to compare data from different data sets.

- Determine the scale of your graph.

- Each grouping of bars should be labeled with the data description and its value.

- Use color and fills to indicate any other groupings the bars represent.

- Label all components of your graph. Indicate what is measured and any other information that will help others understand your graph.

Label your scale and indicate major lines within the graph. Make sure to title your graph.

Interpreting Graphs

Graphs allow those reading them to make predictions. For example, you can extrapolate data by extending the line beyond the points that you plotted using your data. This allows you to predict data you haven't even collected. If you estimate data between plotted points, you have interpolated data.

When you read a graph, you can also determine slope. Slope is the steepness of the line and is the ratio of vertical change (rise or change in y) over the horizontal change (run or change in x). Learning to interpret graphs allows you to understand mathematical relationships between variables. Some common relationships are shown in the chart below.

Critical Measurements
The Quest for Exactness

"Accuracy is a statement of how close measurement results are to the true value. Precision is a measure of how close repeated measurement results are to each other at a specific time under specific conditions. At NIST, we need to strive for both accuracy and precision as the measurements we make permeate the entire U.S. economy."

—Dan Sawyer
Mechanical Engineer, Precision Engineering Division, NIST

NIST
National Institute of
Standards and Technology

Dan Sawyer

Dan Sawyer and his coworkers use state-of-the-art tools and techniques to ensure that scientific instruments, measurement tools, and medical products on the market today meet the required standards for accuracy and precision. People can be confident in the measurements they make using these items because of the calibrations performed in laboratories like Dan's.

Meet the Researcher Video
Join Dan behind the scenes and explore how measurement tools and standards used in surgery, engineering, and aeronautics are tested for accuracy and precision.

Mechanical Engineer **NIST**

Read more about Dan online in the JASON Expedition Center.

Peter Haydock/The JASON Project

Photo Credits (left to right): Adamantios/Wikimedia Commons; NASA; AMagill/Wikimedia Commons; Peter Haydock/The JASON Project; José Reynaldo da Fonseca/Wikimedia Commons; Wetzel-Schaefer/Wikimedia Commons; Ryan Kincade/The JASON Project

Your Expedition Goal...

Understand the importance of accurate and precise measurements to help society.

To accomplish your expedition goal successfully, you will need to

- Evaluate systems and standards of measurement.
- Use measurements to describe objects in your environment.
- Discover why SI units are critical for communication among scientists, engineers, industrial partners, and societies.
- Explore how measurements derived from SI units can be used to further describe your physical environment.
- Compare accuracy and precision when analyzing measurement results.
- Assess how technological advancements to measurement tools impact society.

Join the Team

The Argonauts meet with National Institute of Standards and Technology (NIST) mechanical engineer Dan Sawyer in Gaithersburg, MD. Back Row (L to R): Melinda Woods-Carpenter, Sarah Mullins, Martin Kelsey, Marcelo Ancira, Dan Sawyer, Dean Taylor, Karthik Uppaluri, Lisa Conselatore, Kelly Stewart. Front Row (L to R): Kate Burnett, Keiana Yasunaka, Aubrey Gonzalez, Kendra Elie, and Maggy Botros.

Peter Haydock/The JASON Project

HeavyWeightGeek/Wikimedia Commons

Setting the Standard

What do NFL legend Mike Ditka, author Roald Dahl, businesswoman Martha Stewart, and Queen Elizabeth II have in common? They each have had hip replacements. More than 193,000 total hip replacements are performed in the United States each year. Many of these surgeries are on children. Juvenile rheumatoid arthritis (JRA) is a condition that affects about one in 1,000 children every year, and those who suffer from the disease often need a hip replacement.

Your hip joint is a ball and socket. In healthy people, this joint is able to move freely. However, medical issues, injury, or simply wear and tear can lead to hip pain. Over time, this can lead to the need for a new hip. The surgery requires that the hip socket be re-shaped, and then a metal piece is implanted. The top of the femur is then replaced with an artificial ball. The fit of this new joint needs to be exact. If it does not fit, there will be more pain. Eventually, another surgery might be necessary.

Dan Sawyer and his co-workers at the National Institute of Standards and Technology (NIST) work to develop standards and test procedures so others can make precise and accurate measurements. NIST staff are building instruments and designing tests to ensure that the measurement tools that doctors use are accurate. Without these measurement tools, artificial hips might not fit correctly.

Airplane manufacturers use the results of NIST measurements to ensure that the instruments they use to measure the dimensions of newly assembled airplanes are performing properly. This helps ensure that each flight is safe and efficient. Even missions to Mars would not be possible without the measurement standards that are provided by Dan Sawyer and the staff at NIST.

▼ Calipers, like this one, are used to measure the thickness of objects and, at times, distances. What are some instances in which you might use calipers in your everyday life?

Sterilgutassistentin/Wikimed

🎬 **Expedition 1 Briefing Video** Prepare for your expedition by viewing this briefing on your objectives. Learn how engineers, like Dan Sawyer, use clues to better understand how measurements communicate information.

In This Stage:

Your expedition goal is accomplished when you:

Know what a measurement is.

Know what SI units are.

Know how measurements are standardized.

Why this is important:

Measurements are a part of everyday life. Learning to make and communicate measurements allows us to better interact with our environment.

Words to Identify

precise, accurate, measurement, metrology, length, time, mass, temperature, electric current, amount of substance, luminous intensity, estimate, cubit, metric system, SI units, meter, kilogram, second, ampere, kelvin, mole, candela

Expedition Briefing

Stage 1: Communicating with Measurements

What is a Measurement?

How far is it to your school? How long did you sleep last night? What is the temperature outside? Every day, you encounter many questions similar to these. The process of determining the values of these quantities is called measurement. **Measurement** uses numbers to describe processes and events. If you want to communicate this information, you need to use a common unit of measure. For length, one common unit is the meter.

Common units for length allow us to describe the distance between Earth and other planets. Length can also describe the size of a bacterial cell living on your hand or how tall you are.

Our Ocean Planet

The fact that our planet is not flat poses an interesting challenge for navigation, exploration, and mapping, as Earth's curvature affects measured distances.

Imagine trying to measure the distance from one side of a basketball to the other using only a ruler. It would be difficult because the ruler does not curve with the basketball. Instead, you could wrap a string around the basketball and then measure that length of string.

Nautical miles are similar to this string example, except that they are determined by imaginary lines of latitude that circle the globe. A nautical mile is 1/60th of a degree, one minute of latitude, or 6,076 feet. A nautical mile is almost 800 feet longer than a mile (5,280 ft). If you are ever boating on the ocean, it might be wise to double check how distances are measured on your map because you do not want to miscalculate distance when you are at sea.

Quantities you can measure include:

- **length** – the distance between two points,
- **time** – the interval between two events,
- **mass** – the amount of matter in an object,
- **temperature** – the amount of energy within a sample of matter,
- **electric current** – the flow of charges,
- **amount of substance** – the number of atoms or molecules in a sample of material, and
- **luminous intensity** – the measure of light intensity coming from a source.

Metrology is the study of measurement. This term comes from the Greek words *metron* which means "measure" and *logos* which means "study of." Dan Sawyer is a mechanical engineer who works in the field of metrology at the National Institute of Standards and Technology (NIST). NIST staff help ensure confidence in the measurements made by scientists and engineers who work in critical U.S. industries.

What's at Stake?

How do automakers work to make cars safe? How is it possible for people to explore planets millions of kilometers away?

Engineers who perform crash tests pass or fail cars based on small differences in measurements. A few millimeters could mean the difference between an airbag deploying and passengers being able to walk away from a crash unharmed, or the airbag not deploying and passengers having serious injuries after an accident.

The engineers at the National Aeronautical and Space Administration (NASA) know that during a launch, each kilogram counts. One extra kilogram added to the load has the potential to cost a mission thousands of extra dollars. Therefore, NASA relies on engineers, like Dan Sawyer, to ensure that the measuring instruments they use are accurate. If the tools are not accurate, missions to Mars might not be possible.

Check for Understanding

✓ Why are measurements important?

✓ What can happen if there are errors in measurement?

jonseidman1988/Wikimedia Commons

Temari 09/Wikimedia Commons

JessicaSarahS/Wikimedia Commons

Estimation

Without using a watch, would you know how long it took you to get to school today? Would it be easy to time a race without a stopwatch? In order to do these tasks, you could count out a rhythmic phrase such as "one Mississippi, two Mississippi." This is called an estimate. An **estimate** is an approximate measurement of an object or event. But how do you know your counts are exactly one second apart? You do not know. Estimates performed without measuring tools can vary significantly.

Estimates can also be made by using measuring tools. For example, if you used the second hand on a clock to time a 100-meter dash, you may still need to make an estimate as to whether the runner finished in 16 or 16.5 seconds. The relative accuracy of the tools you use will help you make estimates that are closer to the actual value. When people need to make more accurate measurements, such as in Olympic skiing or swimming races, they may use electronic timers on a watch, phone, or computer to better estimate to the tenths, hundredths, or thousandths of a second.

Check for Understanding

✔ How are estimates made?

Fast Fact

On April 20, 2010, the British Petroleum (BP) Deepwater Horizon oil rig exploded in the Gulf of Mexico. It was the worst off-shore oil spill in U.S. history.

When the explosion occurred, BP and government officials were not able to measure the exact amount of leaking oil. So, engineers made estimates by comparing pressure readings from the leaking well to those from a model of a closed system. By seeing how fast oil could flow, they could estimate how much oil was leaking.

In the end, 4.7 to 8.6 million barrels of oil spilled into the Gulf before the well was capped on July 15, 2010. This picture shows what the oil spill looked like from space.

NASA

Worldwide System of Measurement

Early Measurement

The **cubit** has been identified as one of the earliest recorded measurements. Ancient Egyptians defined the cubit as the length of a person's arm from the elbow to the fingertips. But, was using the body to measure practical?

Compare the sizes of your classmates' hands. What do you notice? It is likely that no two hands are the same size. Because hands come in a wide range of sizes, using a hand to make a measurement could result in a wide range of values.

In ancient Egypt, accurate measurements were important for ambitious building projects, like the Great Pyramid of Giza. To standardize the cubit, Egyptians developed the "royal cubit," thought to be based on the Pharaoh's arm. A master royal cubit of black granite was used as a standard against which all cubits were measured.

A Common System of Measurement

Only a few hundred years ago, people were much more isolated. But as technology has improved, the world has become more connected. For example, many items, like your TV or your clothing, may have been shipped from countries overseas. And many countries collaborate on projects, including the International Space Station.

Imagine if the Russians, Japanese, and Americans on the International Space Station were trying to fix an oxygen pump. What would happen if they all used different systems of measurement?

As people from around the world started working together, the need for a common language to communicate measurements became essential. In 1585, the decimal system began to be used. This is considered the beginning of what would come to be called the metric system.

José Reynaldo da Fonseca/Wikimedia Commons

TheJosh/Wikimedia Commons

Try This!
Use your hand to measure the width of your desk. Compare your measurements with your classmates'. What did you notice? If you could only use your hands to measure objects, how could you be sure that your measurements were as consistent as possible?

The Metric System

The **metric system** is a base-ten system created by Gabriel Mouton in 1670. In this type of system, as the decimal point moves left or right, numbers are multiplied or divided by a factor of ten.

While most countries currently use the metric system exclusively, there are still some which do not. The United States currently uses the metric system in scientific laboratories, while the U.S. customary system is commonly used in everyday measurements.

For example, if you look at the label on a bottle of water in the United States, you may see both systems used. The bottle of water might have ounces (oz) followed by the metric units of milliliters (mL). A label on water bottled in a different country might only list metric units. And although some road signs include distances to landmarks in kilometers, most signs in the United States only display distances in miles.

SI Units

The International System of Units is known as SI from its French name *Systeme International d'Unites*. This is what we know as the modern metric system. **SI units** are the current world standard for measurement.

There are seven basic SI units. They are the **meter**, **kilogram**, **second**, **ampere**, **kelvin**, **mole**, and **candela**. Each unit is used to measure a particular quantity. Additionally, SI units can be combined to describe area, volume, density, speed, and acceleration.

Check for Understanding

✓ What is the metric system?

✓ Provide examples of situations in which you would need to use each of the seven SI units.

SI Base Units

Meter (m)
Base Unit for Length (the distance between two points). Measured as the distance traveled by light in a vacuum in 1/299,792,458 of a second. One meter is about 8.6 cm longer than a yard, and is approximately 39.37 inches or 3.28 feet.

Luigi Chiesa/Wikimedia Commons

Kilogram (kg)
Base Unit for Mass (the amount of matter in an object). In 1889, the physical standard for the kilogram was cast from platinum and iridium. However, the mass of the standard has changed over time. Therefore, NIST scientists are currently working to create a new kilogram standard whose mass will not change.

GregL/Wikimedia Commons

Second (s)
Base Unit for Time (the interval between two events). One second is equal to one tick of a clock. More precisely, the atomic second is determined by the natural frequency of a photon released by a cesium-133 atom.

Jorge Barrios/Wikimedia Commons

Ampere (A)
Base Unit for Electric Current (the flow of charges). One ampere is the amount of force that an electric current exerts between two parallel conductors within a vacuum. Typically, a cell phone requires just less than one ampere to run for one hour.

Adamantios/Wikimedia Commons

Kelvin (K)
Base Unit for Temperature (the amount of energy within a sample of matter). The Kelvin scale is an extension of the Celsius scale. The Kelvin scale extends down to a hypothetical temperature known as absolute zero, or the complete absence of thermal energy. Absolute zero (0K) equals -273.16°C or -459.67°F.

Don/Wikimedia Commons

Mole (mol)
Base Unit for Amount of Substance (the number of atoms or molecules in a sample). The mole measures the physical quantity of a substance. One mole of a particular substance contains 6.022×10^{23} atoms of that substance. There are approximately 5.07 moles of gold in one kilogram of pure gold.

Ryan Kincade/The JASON Project

Candela (Cd)
Base Unit for Luminous Intensity (the measure of light intensity coming from a source). A candela measures the intensity of light. A typical candle has a luminous intensity of about one candela while a 100 watt incandescent bulb is approximately 150 candelas.

4028mdk09/Wikimedia Commons

Schaefer/Wikimedia Commons

Bwsmith84/Wikimedia Commons

Howell Walker/National Geographic Society

SI Prefixes

We use numbers in science, math, and everyday life. They help describe the quantity, or amount, of something. And the size of the numbers used can vary greatly. For example, the distance between Earth and Mars changes throughout the year. They are about 54,500,000,000 meters apart when they are closest together, and around 400,000,000,000 meters when they are furthest apart. Since these figures have a large number of zeros, they can sometimes be awkward to work with.

To turn numbers into a more convenient format, we can use **scientific prefixes**. This allows us to reduce the number of zeros and make the figures more manageable. For example, 54,500,000,000 meters = 54.5 giga-meters, and 400,000,000,000 meters = 400 gigameters. Using the prefix "giga" can make it much easier to multiply and divide these numbers. Scientific prefixes can also help us form a mental picture of the numbers being discussed.

"Kilo" means *1,000* in Greek. "Milli" means *1,000* in Latin. For the prefixes of the SI units, both Greek and Latin are used. When "kilo" is in front of a base unit, it means 1,000 times bigger than the base unit. When "milli" is in front of a base unit, it means 1,000 times smaller than the base unit.

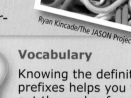

Ryan Kincade/The JASON Project

Vocabulary

Knowing the definitions of prefixes helps you to figure out the scale of root words. There are many common words, which also use scientific prefixes. For example, a decathlon is an athletic event with 10 (deka) events. A decathlete is the athlete who competes in the 10 (deka) events. Can you figure out what some of the following words mean?

decibel, decimal, deciliter, centigrade, cent, centigram, millibar, milligram, milliliter, nanogram, microgram

SI Prefixes in the Metric System

Prefix	Symbol	Multiplier	Base Unit in Meters
Giga-	G	10^9 or 1,000,000,000	The diameter of the sun is approximately 1.4 gigameters.
Mega-	M	10^6 or 1,000,000	The distance from Atlanta, GA, to Washington, DC, is about one megameter.
Kilo-	k	10^3 or 1,000	It takes about 1,390 steps to walk one kilometer.
Hecto-	h	10^2 or 100	The length of an NFL football field measures just over one hectometer.
Deka-	da	10^1 or 10	The height of a three-story building is about one dekameter.
Base Unit		1	A baseball bat is about one meter long.
Deci-	d	10^{-1} or 0.1	The length of a cell phone is about one decimeter.
Centi-	c	10^{-2} or 0.01	A fingernail is about one centimeter wide.
Milli-	m	10^{-3} or 0.001	The wire in a paperclip is about one millimeter in diameter.
Micro-	μ	10^{-6} or 0.000001	A typical red blood cell has a diameter of about six to eight micrometers.
Nano-	n	10^{-9} or 0.000000001	A water molecule is less than one nanometer wide.

Converting Metric Units

Each unit in the metric system increases or decreases by a factor of 10, relative to the base unit. This makes the math much more simple than with customary measurements. If you are converting from millimeters to kilometers, you just need to know that there are 10 millimeters in a centimeter, 10 centimeters in a decimeter, 10 decimeters in meter, 10 meters in a dekameter, 10 dekameters in a hectometer, and 10 hectometers in a kilometer. That may be a lot of steps away, but all you have to remember is the number 10. And it is easy to multiply or divide by 10.

When you are converting from a big unit (like kilometers) to a smaller unit (like millimeters), you multiply. This is because there are more of the smaller units in the bigger unit. When you multiply by 10, you just add a zero to the original number.

10 × 10 = 100 (which is a 10 with another zero)

This is the same as moving the decimal one place to the right.

1,000 × 10 = 10,000 (which is 1,000 with another zero)

All whole numbers can be written with a decimal. But where was the decimal in 1,000?

1,000 is the same as 1,000.0

When you are converting from a small unit (like millimeters) to a larger unit (like kilometers) you divide. When you divide by 10, you take away a zero. You can think of this as moving the decimal place one position to the left. And, what happens when you run out of zeros? You add a decimal in front of your unit.

1,000 / 10 = 100 (which is 1,000 with one less zero)

1 / 10 = 0.1

If you are starting with a number that already has a decimal, like 0.0001, to divide by 10, you move the decimal one place to the left.

0.0001 / 10 = 0.00001

Do not forget that when you are moving the decimal to the left, you have to add a zero as a placeholder.

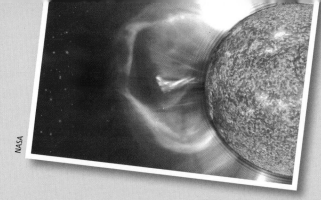

NASA

When converting from a unit that is really far away from the unit you are converting to, you can combine some of those 10s. Millimeters are three steps away from meters, so you can multiply 10 × 10 × 10 (three steps, three 10s) to equal 1,000. So there are 1,000 millimeters in a meter.

Since we know the conversions from millimeters to kilometers, we know that a million millimeters is equal to one kilometer.

Check for Understanding

✓ When would you use a scientific prefix?

✓ Describe one way to convert units.

Once on Mars, the rover *Curiosity* will travel as far as 20,000 meters across the planet's surface. To find out how many kilometers the rover will travel, convert meters to kilometers. Here is one way to convert units.

CONVERTING UNITS

1 Identify the number and the base you want to convert.

The rover Curiosity will travel up to **20,000 m** across the surface of Mars.

2 Write the conversion factor for the measurement you are trying to figure out. Make sure the unit you want to convert to is written as the numerator.

1 kilometer **equals** 1,000 meters:

$$\frac{1 \text{ km}}{1,000 \text{ m}}$$

3 Multiply the number you want to convert by the conversion factor.

$$20,000 \text{ m} \times \frac{1 \text{ km}}{1,000 \text{ m}}$$

$$= \frac{20,000 \text{ m}}{1} \times \frac{1 \text{ km}}{1,000 \text{ m}}$$

$$= \frac{20,000 \text{ m} \cdot \text{km}}{1,000 \text{ m}}$$

$$= 20 \text{ km}$$

Jeancaffou/Wikimedia Commons

U.S. Customary Units

Think back to the last time you poured a glass of milk. If you live in the United States, chances are you poured your milk from a gallon jug. A gallon is one of the U.S. customary units, which are the standard units of measurement commonly used in the United States.

Although most industrialized nations use SI units for almost all of their measurements, the United States uses them primarily for military and scientific purposes. The United States continues to use its own customary system for everyday measurements. The amount of food in packages and recipes, the speed of cars, and even official land measurements are all indicated in U.S. customary units.

If you live in the United States, you are probably more familiar with the U.S. customary system than the SI system. For example, you probably know how tall you are in feet and inches, the U.S. customary units of length, rather than meters and centimeters. When you check in the morning to see if you will need a coat, you likely find the day's temperature in Fahrenheit rather than Celsius.

In 1988, the U.S. government passed legislation designating the SI system as its preferred system of measurement. In fact, most U.S. customary units are now standardized against SI units. Since then, the United States has slowly moved toward incorporating the SI system in everyday life.

▲ In some regions of the United States, road signs reflect both U.S. customary units and SI units.

Check for Understanding

✓ What are some examples of U.S. customary units, and when are they used?

The Importance of Units

Imagine you are riding your bicycle to the post office for the first time. On the way, you get lost. When you stop and ask for directions, you are told, "Bike two, turn left, and then bike three."

You would probably be confused by those directions. What do the numbers "two" and "three" mean? They could describe anything—feet, meters, or even miles. Three meters and three kilometers are very different.

When communicating a measurement, it is important to include the units. Measurements such as length, time, weight, area, volume, and density, can be confusing without units.

What if that person gave you units but used different units for each measure? For instance, what if they said, "Bike two kilometers down that way, turn left, and then bike another three miles." Would you know the total distance you would have to travel?

Converting Customary and Metric Units

1. Identify the numbers and units in the problem.

   Bike two kilometers down Elm Street, turn left, and then bike another three miles.

2. Choose the units you are converting to and from.

   3 miles to kilometers (km)

3. Determine the conversion factor between the different units.

   1 mile = 1.6 km

4. Multiply your original number by the conversion factor.

   $$\frac{3 \text{ miles}}{1} \times \frac{1.6 \text{ km}}{1 \text{ mile}}$$

5. Cancel the units where you can, and solve the math.

   $$\frac{3 \text{ miles}}{1} \times \frac{1.6 \text{ km}}{1 \text{ mile}} = 4.8 \text{ km}$$

6. This should leave you with the proper conversion.

   3 miles = 4.8 km

7. Add the two numbers together to find the total distance traveled.

   2 km + 4.8 km = 6.8 km

Measuring With Tools

Take a look around you. Your life is full of measurements, from the temperature of your surroundings to the number of calories in your midday snack. How many of the objects and energy forms that you observe can be measured? In what way can they be quantified? Can you identify the best tools and techniques to obtain the most reliable measurements?

For Dan Sawyer and the other engineers at NIST, measurements are not just a part of their life—they are their life's work. Dan and his coworkers perform critical calibrations of instruments that measure. Their work covers tools that make different types of measurements, including time, temperature, length, mass, and volume.

In this activity, you will take a closer look at measurement. Through observation, inquiry, and analysis, you will develop a better understanding of measurement concepts as you move from station to station.

Materials
- Lab 1 Data Sheet
- materials provided by your instructor

Lab Prep

1. When you enter the laboratory, do not touch any of the stations. Wait for instructions before beginning the lab.

2. With your instructor, review all appropriate laboratory procedures, safety guidelines, and classroom rules.

3. Review the objectives and any procedures that are established for each station.

4. Review the order in which you will move from station to station.

Make Observations

1. When your instructor is ready, a signal will be given to begin work at your first station. Remember that you only have a limited amount of time to work at each station and answer questions.

2. Use the tools and materials provided at each station to perform the suggested investigation.

Reflect and Apply

1. Why do you need different tools to measure different things?

2. Outside of this lab, where have you seen or used measurements?

3. What challenges have you encountered when making measurements?

Extension

Select one of the measurement types (e.g., time, length, temperature) you explored and devise a different tool to measure it. With your teacher's permission, construct the device, and then calibrate and use it. How does your new device compare to the one you created and used previously?

 Journal Question Is it essential to always identify a measurement standard? Explain.

▲ One tool developed to measure temperature is known as the Galileo thermometer. This tool consists of a long vertical tube filled with a clear liquid. Several spheres are placed inside the tube. Each sphere has a slightly different density. As the temperature of the tube changes, the different spheres move up and down the tube, indicating the relative temperature.

C.K.H/flickr

Your expedition goal is accomplished when you:

Know what derived units are.

Know what dimensional analysis is.

Why this is important:

By combining SI units, we can better describe the physical properties of matter.

Words to Identify

derived units, area, volume, displaces, speed, acceleration, weight, force, mass, newton, density

Stage 2: Derived Units

SI Derived Units

Derived units combine SI units to allow people to better describe the world. These derived units use more than one measurement at a time. Some examples include area, volume, density, speed, acceleration, and weight.

Area

Area is the size of the surface of a two-dimensional object. For example, the area of a room is the floor space that could be covered by carpeting. The area of objects can be calculated using mathematical equations that use the SI unit for length.

To calculate how much carpet is needed for a rectangular room, you would measure both the length and the width of the room in meters. You would then multiply the length by the width to get the area. Because you multiply meters by meters to get area, area is always measured in square units, such as square meters (m^2).

Volume

Volume is the amount of space inside a three-dimensional object. For example, an empty shoebox contains space. Larger boxes have more space inside. The volume of a shoebox can be calculated by multiplying the length, width, and height of the box.

But how can the volume be determined for objects with sides that are not easy to measure? Since it is difficult to measure oddly shaped objects, like rocks and people, a method called water displacement can be used.

When you get into a bathtub, the water level rises. This is because water cannot fill a space if your body is already filling it. Your body **displaces**, or pushes out, an amount of water equal to the volume of your body below the water line.

You can measure the amount of water displaced by an object by putting the object into a graduated cylinder filled part way with water. Record the water level before and after adding the object. A rise of one milliliter (mL) is equal to the volume of one cubic centimeter (cm^3).

Speed

The next time somebody drives you to school, look at the speedometer. This instrument tells the driver how fast this vehicle is going. **Speed** is the change in distance over time. If the speedometer reads 50 mph (80 km/h), driving at this speed for one hour will move you 50 miles (80 km). Speed is a derived unit because it combines length and time.

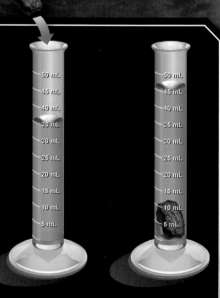

Try This!

Gather a few waterproof objects in a variety of shapes. With your classmates, brainstorm other methods, besides using a graduated cylinder, to measure the volume of these objects. Try some of these methods and compare your results. Did your volume measurements vary with the methods used? Did some methods work for some of the objects and not for others?

Select a cube-shaped object that does not float. Measure the object's length, width, and height, and use the measurements to calculate its volume (volume = length × width × height). Then measure the volume using one of the other methods you tried. How do the two measurements compare? Which do you think is more correct?

Acceleration

Think about a time when you were sitting in a car at a red light. As the light changed from red to green, the driver stepped on the gas pedal, and you may have been pushed back into your seat. This was the feeling of acceleration. **Acceleration** is the rate of the change in velocity. Velocity and acceleration will be discussed further in Expedition 2. But in simple terms, velocity is an object's speed in a particular direction. Acceleration is calculated by dividing the change in velocity by time. It is measured in meters per second squared (m/s^2). The greater the acceleration, the more you will be pushed back.

Weight

Weight is the **force** exerted on any object with mass by the gravitational acceleration of a body such as a planet. Hold a book up and then let it go. What happens? The gravitational acceleration of the planet acting on the mass of the book forces it to the ground. There are two variables that can affect the weight of an object. These are the **mass** of the object and the gravitational acceleration produced by the body that is acting on it. A common misconception is that mass and weight are the same. However, mass is the amount of material or matter in an object and is not a derived unit. Mass is measured in the SI base unit of kilograms (kg).

Weight is calculated by multiplying the mass by the gravitational acceleration at the location of the object. Scientists have determined that the gravitational acceleration on the surface of Earth changes depending on location and time of year. Recent discoveries from satellites continue to uncover how these gravitational differences change. More research is still needed to understand this better, so for now, we use a standard gravitational acceleration of 9.8 m/s^2 for all of our general calculations on Earth. Weight is measured in kilogram meters per second squared, or **newtons**.

If you were to step on a scale on Mars, your weight would be considerably less than on Earth. This is because the gravitational acceleration is less on Mars, about 3.72 m/s^2. Your mass, however, is exactly the same on both planets, and everywhere else in the universe.

Check for Understanding

✓ Compare mass and weight.

Earth vs. Mars

$$\underset{\text{(kg)}}{\text{mass}} \times \underset{\text{(m/s}^2\text{)}}{\text{gravitational acceleration}} = \underset{\text{(N)}}{\text{weight}}$$

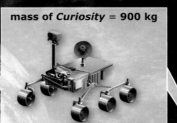

mass of *Curiosity* = 900 kg

▼ The Mars rover *Curiosity* has a mass of 900 kg on both Earth and Mars. However, *Curiosity's* weight on Mars is less than half its weight on Earth.

Gravitational acceleration on Earth: 9.8 m/s^2

$$\underset{\text{mass}}{900 \text{ kg}} \times \underset{\substack{\text{gravitational} \\ \text{acceleration} \\ \text{on Earth}}}{9.8 \text{ m/s}^2} =$$

$$\underset{\substack{\text{weight of } Curiosity \\ \text{on Earth}}}{8,820 \text{ N}}$$

Gravitational acceleration on the surface of Mars: 3.72 m/s^2

$$\underset{\text{mass}}{900 \text{ kg}} \times \underset{\substack{\text{gravitational} \\ \text{acceleration} \\ \text{on Mars}}}{3.72 \text{ m/s}^2} =$$

$$\underset{\substack{\text{weight of } Curiosity \\ \text{on Mars}}}{3,348 \text{ N}}$$

not to scale

NASA

Density

Density is the amount of mass in a given volume. All solids, liquids, and gases have density, though the densities can be affected by temperature and pressure. You can sometimes "feel" density by holding two objects of the same size but different weights, such as a bowling ball and a volley-ball. Although they are about the same shape and size, the bowling ball has much more mass than the volleyball. So the bowling ball has a higher density than the volley-ball.

Knowing an object's density allows you to predict whether the object will float or sink. When there is gravity, objects will sink when placed in a liquid of lesser density. For example, most rocks will sink in water, while foam peanuts will float.

Kr-Val/Wikimedia Commons

Team Highlight

Argonauts Dean Taylor, Kate Burnett, and Kelly Stewart use the NIST measuring tape calibration facility to establish an accurate length standard. This system uses a trolley and a measuring laser to generate accurate lengths. This facility is used to determine if measuring tapes used in construction, ship building, and the petroleum industry are accurate before critical measurements are performed.

Check for Understanding

✓ Why might it be important to know an object's density?

Try This!

Pour some cooking oil into a small bowl. Cover the bowl with aluminum foil and secure the foil, so it cannot come off. Poke a dime-sized hole in the top of the foil. Fill a larger bowl three-quarters of the way with water. Submerge the small bowl in the larger one, holding it on the bottom if necessary. What happens to the oil? Why?

Densities of Common Substances

Substance	Density
Air	0.0013 g/cm³
Hydrogen	0.0001663 g/cm³
Water	1.00 g/cm³
Rubbing Alcohol	0.81 g/cm³
Gasoline	0.66 g/cm³
Milk	1.03 g/cm³

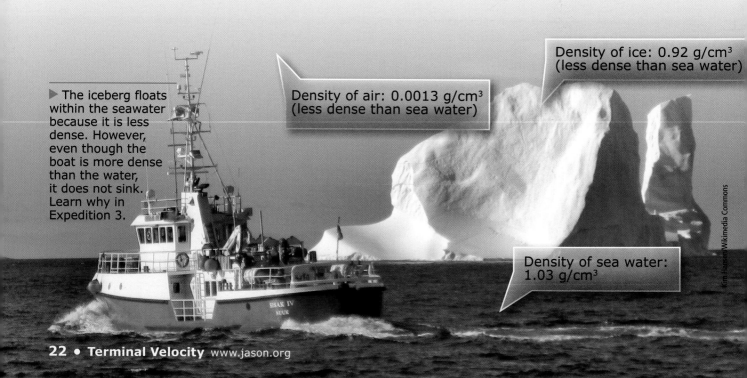

Density of ice: 0.92 g/cm³ (less dense than sea water)

Density of air: 0.0013 g/cm³ (less dense than sea water)

▶ The iceberg floats within the seawater because it is less dense. However, even though the boat is more dense than the water, it does not sink. Learn why in Expedition 3.

Density of sea water: 1.03 g/cm³

Kim Hansen/Wikimedia Commons

Calculating Derived Units

Calculating Speed

Formula:
speed (m/s) = distance (m) / time (s)

Units:
The SI unit for speed is meters per second (m/s).

Example:
If you traveled 200 m in 20 seconds, what was your speed?

speed = 200 m / 20 s

Your speed was 10 m/s.

Iam McWilliams / Wikimedia Commons

Calculating Acceleration

Formula:
acceleration (m/s^2) = change in velocity (m/s) / time (s)

Units:
The SI unit for acceleration is meters per second per second, or meters per second squared (m/s^2).

Example:
If a car moving north changed its velocity from 10 m/s to 30 m/s over a span of 5 s, what was its acceleration?

acceleration = (30 m/s − 10 m/s) / 5 s

The car's acceleration was 4 m/s^2.

Calculating Area

Formula (area of a rectangular prism):
area (m^2) = base (m) × height (m)

Units:
The SI units for area are always squared (e.g., cm^2, m^2, km^2) because area is a two-dimensional measurement.

Example:
If your bedroom is a rectangle that measures 3 meters by 4 meters, how much carpet would you need to cover the floor?

area = 3 m × 4 m

You would need 12 m^2 of carpet.

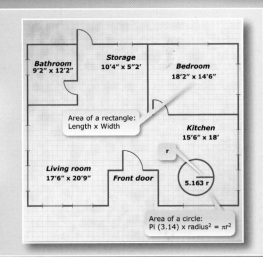

Bathroom
9'2" x 12'2"

Storage
10'4" x 5"2'

Bedroom
18'2" x 14'6"

Area of a rectangle:
Length x Width

Kitchen
15'6" x 18'

Living room
17'6" x 20'9"

Front door

5.163 r

Area of a circle:
Pi (3.14) x radius^2 = πr^2

Calculating Volume

Formula (volume of a rectangular prism):
volume (m^3) = length (m) × width (m) × height (m)

Units:
The SI units for area are always cubed (e.g., cm^3, m^3, km^3) because volume is a three-dimensional measurement.

Example:
If you are filling up a window planter that is 20 cm long, 8 cm deep, and 6 cm high, how much potting soil would you need?

volume = 20 cm × 8 cm × 6 cm

The volume of the planter is 960 cm^3, so you will need 960 cm^3 of potting soil.

Calculating Density

Formula:
density (kg/m^3) = mass (kg) / volume (m^3)

Units:
The SI unit for density is kilogram per meters cubed (kg/m^3).

Example:
If a 5 kg block of metal has a volume of 2 m^3, what is the density of the metal?

density = 5 kg / 2 m^3

The density is 2.5 kg/m^3.

Measuring Mysteries

As part of his job as an engineer at NIST, Dan Sawyer has access to some of the most sophisticated measurement tools in the world. However, you can make measurements using simple tools found in the laboratory. Further, you can even make your own measurement tools, including a density column. Density columns feature several layers of liquid with different densities.

In this lab, you will be provided with several unknown substances and will use them to create a density column. You will then use your density column to compare the densities of other unknown substances.

Materials

- Lab 2 Data Sheet
- 6 small graduated cylinders (no more than 25 mL) OR 6 small paper cups marked to 25 mL
- 1 large graduated cylinder (100 mL)
- 1 rubber stopper
- 1 small bolt
- 1 small cork
- 1 ruler
- electronic balance
- funnel
- yellow mystery liquid
- blue mystery liquid
- orange mystery liquid
- green mystery liquid
- red mystery liquid
- amber mystery liquid

Lab Prep

1. Put on your safety goggles.

2. Use the balance and your graduated cylinders or cups to determine the mass and volume of your three initial mystery liquids. Calculate the density of each liquid using the formula: density = mass / volume.

3. Next, order the density of the liquids from least dense to most dense. Pour them into the large graduated cylinder from most dense to least dense to see if you were correct. This is your density column.

Make Observations

1. Using any combination of the scale, ruler, water, and large graduated cylinder, determine the density of your rubber stopper, metal bolt, and cork. Based on your calculations, order the solids by density, from least dense to most dense.

2. Confirm your calculations using your density column. Start by putting your densest item into your large graduated cylinder. More dense substances will sink, while less dense float.

3. Once you have assembled all of your substances, take a look at your density column. Compare it to a neighboring lab group. Do your columns look similar? Why or why not?

4. Your teacher will give you three additional mystery liquids.

5. Record the volume of your first mystery liquid and pour it into your density column very slowly. Give the liquid a few seconds to settle into place. It should form a distinctive layer in the density column.

6. Based on where the mystery liquid settles into the column, make an estimate as to what the liquid's density might be.

7. Using the estimated density and the known volume of your mystery liquid, calculate the mass of your mystery liquid.

8. Repeat steps 5—7 for the two additional mystery liquids.

9. Your instructor will give you a data sheet of liquids and their densities. Use this data sheet to name all six of the liquids you used in this experiment.

Reflect and Apply

1. How did your calculations compare to what you observed?

2. When might you need to use this knowledge outside of the classroom?

 Journal Question Describe how you determined the density of these liquids and solids.

In This Stage:

Your expedition goal is accomplished when you:

Know what accuracy is.

Know what precision is.

Know how we ensure the accuracy and precision of measurements.

Why this is important:

As technology advances, so does the need to be more accurate and precise. Measurement errors could endanger people and property.

Words to Identify

standard, calibration, compensation, accuracy, precision, significant digits, random errors, systematic errors

Stage 3: Accuracy and Precision

Setting High Standards for Measurement

When building a school, all of the measuring tools used by the builders must be accurate. If they are not accurate, windows and doors might not fit properly. Critical supports might be placed in the wrong location, leading to a catastrophic failure. If the International Space Station was not built using accurate measuring tools, countries would not be able to reliably attach their spacecraft and board the station.

One aspect of Dan Sawyer's job is to provide accurate standards so companies can determine if their measuring instruments can perform their tasks accurately. A **standard** is a benchmark used to compare other measures.

Even a small measurement error in the building of a passenger airplane could cost an airline company thousands of dollars in wasted fuel. It could also put lives at risk. Without standards, missions to Mars would be impossible. Small mistakes could mean a huge risk—both in terms of money and lives.

Calibration and Compensation

The next time you are in a grocery store, look at the scales in the produce section. When nothing is in the basket, is the arrow pointing right at the zero? If not, you could end up paying too much for your apples.

Tools such as scales help us perform tasks more efficiently. But before we can use the data collected from these tools, they need to be calibrated. **Calibration** is the process of determining how close a measured result is to the true value. For instance, if a 0.50 kg weight is placed in a scale, and the scale reads 0.50 kg, the scale has been calibrated because the difference between the scale reading and the true value is zero. If the difference is too large, the scale might need to be adjusted.

Many scales have a knob that can be used to adjust the reading so that it is the exact value of a known weight. This adjustment is known as **compensation**. But because very few things stay the same, the scale might need to be calibrated in the future to determine if it needs to be compensated again.

Check for Understanding

✓ Why are standards important?

✓ Why do you need to calibrate tools?

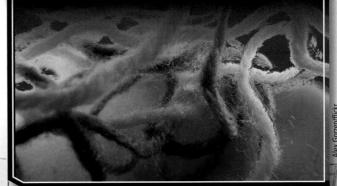

Try This!

Cut a 30-cm length of yarn. Have a classmate cut another piece of yarn of identical length using the yarn you cut as the standard. Using this new piece of yarn as the new standard, have another classmate cut a piece of yarn of identical length. Continue until every member of the class has cut a piece of yarn.

Using the ruler, measure the pieces of yarn that were cut. How close are they to 30 centimeters? Now compare the lengths of all the pieces of yarn. Are the pieces approximately the same size? If they are not the right length or are not similar in size, what could have caused these errors?

Alex Gorzen/flickr

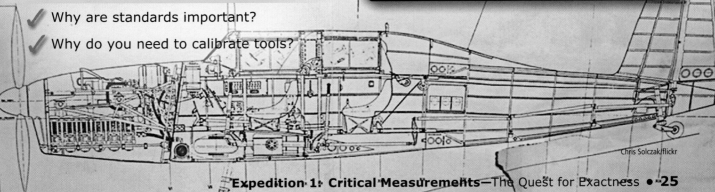

Chris Solczak/flickr

Accuracy versus Precision

If you measured the length of your classroom ten times in a row, do you think you would get the exact same measurement all ten times? Even if you did, would they necessarily be correct? Precision and accuracy are two important components of measurement. **Accuracy** is how close your measurement is to the actual value. **Precision** is how close a group of measurements are to each other.

The next time you play darts, try hitting the bullseye with every throw. Accuracy comes when the darts hit the bullseye. Precision comes when the darts hit the same area, but not necessarily near the bullseye.

If the darts hit the upper right hand corner of the dartboard every time, then you are precise but not accurate. If every dart hits the bullseye, you are both accurate and precise. If the darts hit all over the dart board, but not the bullseye, you are neither precise nor accurate.

Confidence in Measurement

Knowing that your measurements are correct is very important. For Dan Sawyer, it is critical. But there is no such thing as a perfect measurement. Every measurement, as well as every measurement tool, contains a certain amount of error. Measurements are limited by the tools used to make them. If the tools are off, then the measurements taken with the tools will be off as well.

For example, when NIST tests a tape measure, the largest potential error comes from the thickness of the line that indicates a measurement. The thicker the line is, the harder it is to estimate its center and the greater the potential error in determining the actual center of the line.

In addition, tension in the tape measure always needs to be monitored. Changes in tension affect the length of the measured tape. Dan constantly monitors tension and other factors because he knows that errors they introduce will affect everything measured with these tools.

Significant Digits

Significant digits describe how precise a number is. There are several rules to follow when counting significant digits:

1. Any zero digits that are "sandwiched" by non zero digits are significant.
   5,000,035 = 7 significant digits

2. Zeros that lead non zero digits do not count.
   0.000087 = 2 significant digits

3. If there is a decimal point, zeros that trail non zero digits count.
   0.00045000 = 5 significant digits

4. If there is no decimal point, trailing zeros after whole numbers do not count.
   340,000 = 2 significant digits

5. If there is a decimal point after a whole number, all digits are significant.
   340,000.0 = 7 significant digits

▼ Which ruler will result in greater precision if used to take repeated measurements? Why?

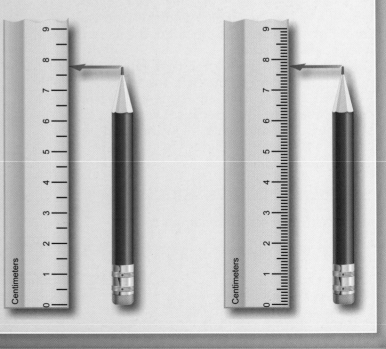

Bogdan Suditu/Flickr

Measuring Tape Calibration Laboratory

Have you ever wondered how manufacturers of different measuring instruments, like steel rulers and measuring tapes, ensure that the instruments are accurate? In order to perform accurate measurements, the graduation markings on the instruments must be carefully placed at exact intervals. How is this done? Do manufacturers use a master tape or ruler to make other new ones? How are master rulers calibrated? The answer to these questions can be found in the measuring tape calibration laboratory at the National Institute of Standards and Technology (NIST) in Gaithersburg, MD. Scientists and engineers at NIST have constructed a unique laser measuring device that is used to calibrate the master rulers and tapes used by manufacturers to ensure the accuracy of the millions of tapes produced every year.

The measuring device includes a bench, which is approximately 60 meters long, or about the distance from the nose to the tail of a large commercial airplane. The master tape is laid flat on the bench and a specified tension is applied along the length. This tension is required because steel tapes can stretch depending on the amount of force applied during measurement. A carriage with a microscope is positioned so that the markings on the tape are visible through the microscope. The carriage can be positioned over any of the lines on the tape. The displacement of the carriage between lines on the tape is measured using the NIST reference laser interferometer. Because objects can change length depending on their temperature, by international agreement, a reference temperature is defined at 20°C. Length is defined at 20°C; therefore, the temperature in Dan's laboratory is carefully controlled to 20°C ± 0.15°C.

Peter Haydock/The JASON Project

Measuring Device: A microscope carriage with active wavelength compensated helium-neon laser interferometer that realizes the definition of the international meter.

Measuring Facility: 80 meters long and temperature controlled to 20°C ± 0.15°C. Material temperature sensors and air sensors placed every 10 meters along the 60 meter bench. Barometric pressure and relative humidity measurements are recorded and used to compensate for the laser light wavelength.

Measurement Accuracy: The measuring tape calibrations are accurate to about 0.2 mm over the entire 60 meter length of the bench. Even the entire length of a large commercial airplane can be measured to this level of accuracy.

Errors in Measurement

Measurement errors can be divided into two categories: random or systematic. **Random errors** are not always predictable. They can come from the instruments themselves, or from environmental issues.

Imagine doing a physics experiment in class. You measure the height a ball bounces, but it is hard to see the exact top of the bounce height. Each time, your measurement varies slightly. This error would affect the results of your experiment. To reduce the random error in this case, you can take the average of your measurements.

The other type of error is systematic. **Systematic errors** are predictable, but not always preventable. Systematic errors can come from uncalibrated tools or inconsistencies in other factors that affect the measurement being performed.

An example of a systematic error that Dan Sawyer needs to be aware of is temperature. An error in the measured temperature of a tape can significantly affect his measurement results since the tapes can expand or contract.

To help reduce this error, Dan places a calibrated thermometer every 10 meters along his measuring bench. This way he can more accurately estimate the actual temperature of the tape. If systematic errors can be identified, they can be calculated and used to find the correct answer. This results in higher accuracy.

Check for Understanding

✓ Compare random and systematic errors.

Impact of Measurement

Measurements are found throughout our world. From weighing apples at the grocery store to calculating how long it takes to get home from school, chances are you encounter measurements every day.

Errors can cause problems by leading to measurements that are neither accurate nor precise. Sometimes these problems can be minor, but they can also cause major problems. For example, a calculation error in determining a car's stopping distance on a road could result in a deadly accident.

Dan Sawyer and the staff at NIST provide standards and measurement so that our everyday life is safe and efficient. Their work reminds us why we should care about measurements and why accuracy and precision are important.

Team Highlight

Chris Blackburn, a physical science technician from NIST, shows the Argonauts how a portable coordinate measuring machine (CMM) can measure different three-dimensional objects, including gears and his hand.

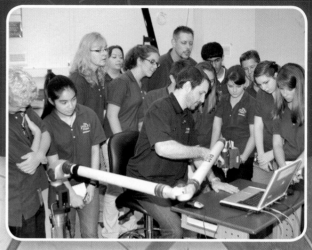

Peter Haydock/The JASON Project

Check for Understanding

✓ Describe the difference between accuracy and precision.

This archer was accurate, since all of the arrows are within the inner circle of the target. He was not precise, since the arrows are spread throughout the inner circle. This was likely caused by random error.

This archer was precise—all of the arrows are grouped closely together. However, he was not accurate, since the arrows are not near the bullseye. This was likely caused by a systematic error, such as poor bow tension.

Accurate

Precise

Not Accurate or Precise

Systematic errors reduce accuracy

Random errors reduce precision

This archer was both precise and accurate, since the arrows are grouped closely together and around the bullseye.

This archer was neither precise nor accurate, since the arrows are spread around the target and not near the bullseye.

cobaltfish/flickr

Targeting Accuracy and Precision

Accuracy is how close a measurement is to the actual measurement. Precision is how close repeated measurements are to each other. These two concepts are the foundation of all work done by Dan Sawyer and the scientists and engineers at NIST. The accuracy and precision of the tools they test are critical in many ways. A small mistake can cost hundreds of thousands of dollars for users, as in the case of airplane manufacturers.

In this activity, you will explore precision and accuracy. You will determine how accurate or precise you are in completing various challenges. Then you will create a model to demonstrate precision and accuracy.

Materials
- Lab 3 Data Sheet
- stopwatch
- water
- graduated cylinder
- pencil
- 3 cups
- drawing paper
- safety goggles
- materials provided by instructor

Lab Prep

1. Work with a partner to identify the difference between accuracy and precision by completing the following challenges:

   a. Have your partner start a stopwatch. Tell your partner when you think 30 seconds has elapsed. Your partner will not tell you if you are correct, but will record the actual elapsed time. Repeat this activity three times, and graph your results.

   b. Fill a cup with what you think is 25 mL of water. Repeat this activity three times. Then measure the amount of water using a graduated cylinder and graph your results.

   c. Draw a circle that has a diameter of 4 cm. Repeat this three times. Then measure to see if you were correct. Graph your results.

2. With your partner, look at each of your results. Label your results to show which ones were accurate, which ones were precise, which results were both accurate and precise, and which results were neither accurate nor precise. Then, define precision and accuracy in your own words.

Make Observations

1. Work with a partner to engineer a model that can demonstrate both precision and accuracy. An example could be a catapult trying to reach a target or a car that can stop at a designated point.

2. Put on your safety goggles. With your instructor's approval, assemble and test your model.

Reflect and Apply

1. From what you observe, can you improve your design? Consider your observations as you improve the design of your model.

Extension

Test your accuracy and precision by measuring and recording the length of an object five times. How precise are your measurements? How could you determine how accurate your measurements are? How could you increase the accuracy of your five measurements? Repeat this activity measuring volume and mass.

 Journal Question Which is more important, accuracy or precision? Explain. Describe some cases where one quality would be more important than the other.

Measurements in Your Home

Architects, contractors, electricians, plumbers, and others involved in building a new home must use careful, exact measurements. Here are some examples:

1 To build a safe, secure home, carpenters and builders use measuring tapes to measure the **length** (meters) of wood and other materials.

2 To mix strong, durable cement, workers must carefully measure the **volume** (liters) of water and cement mix they combine.

3 Electricians use meters and gauges to measure electrical **current** (amperes) in a home, making sure currents are at safe levels.

4 Lighting levels in a home can be adjusted by using bulbs with different levels of **luminous intensity** (candelas).

5 On a construction site, measuring time can be very important. When workers use solder to join copper pipes, for example, they must wait the right amount of **time** (seconds) for it to cool and harden before they can join the next piece.

HOME insulators

HOME insulators

6 Instruments for measuring temperature are vital on a hot water tank. Keeping the **temperature** (°Celsius) of the water at the right level means the difference between comfortable hot showers and scalding hot water.

7 Crane operators must know the **weight** (newtons) of the heavy object they are lifting to ensure they have the proper equipment to lift it safely.

8 In planning and budgeting for flooring, carpenters must measure and calculate **area** (square meters) in order to know how many tiles they will need to cover the floor.

9 Builders must use scale plans created by architects to determine the **length** (meters) of each component of the house, such as boards and pipes. This ensures that the final product is both safe and strong.

Stringing Along

Recall that your expedition goal is *to understand the importance of accurate and precise measurements to help society*. Now that you are fully briefed, it is time to apply your understanding of measurement to determine if certain measurement tools meet a specified requirement.

We often take for granted that the tools we use to measure objects are both accurate and precise. An error of one millimeter may not mean much in the classroom, but if it is your job to ensure that aircraft, like space shuttles and airplanes, are assembled correctly, one millimeter can cause losses of tens of thousands of dollars. In modern airplane building, the huge wings may be built in one factory, and other parts such as the body and the tail sections built in another. If the scientists, engineers, and technicians in different factories do not use the same unit of length, these expensive and critical parts may not fit together during assembly. Dan Sawyer and other engineers at NIST work hard to ensure that measuring instruments sold in the market are accurate.

Accurate measurements require accurate measuring tools, good measuring techniques, and a thorough understanding of what factors can affect measurements. In the case of measuring tapes, temperature and tension are two primary factors that affect the accuracy of measurements performed. Tapes expand or grow in length when their temperature increases and shrink when the temperature decreases. The amount of force or tension that is applied to the tape while it is in use can also make measurements less accurate. If a tape stretches due to tension, the distances between the graduations increase—making the tapes less accurate.

To begin this Field Assignment, you will examine the effect of temperature on the length of a measuring tape. Once you have completed your examination, you will create a length-measuring tool and analyze the effect of tension (expressed as a function of mass) on this tool in order to make it more accurate.

Materials
- Expedition 1 Field Assignment Data Sheet
- kite string
- duct tape (or strong tape)
- spring scale
- marker
- meter stick
- variety of other types of string

mueritz/flickr

Objectives:
- Graph the measured length of a 40-m measuring tape versus its temperature.
- Analyze the graph to determine the relationship between length and temperature.
- Create a length-measuring device that is sensitive to changes in tension.
- Analyze data to determine how accuracy can be affected.

Field Prep

1. Using Dan Sawyer's data found in the data sheet, graph length versus temperature of a 40-m measuring tape under constant tension. Add a line of best fit through the data points.

2. Using the graph, estimate the length of the measuring tape at 10°C, 20°C, and 30°C.

3. From the graph, describe how temperature affects the length of a measuring tape under constant tension.

4. Describe how this may affect the construction of a building that takes place outside throughout the year in a location where the temperature fluctuates between -30° and 30°C.

5. Research the average temperature fluctuations in your area throughout the year and consider the effects on measurements in your region.

6. Discuss with a classmate how construction workers might need to compensate for temperature fluctuations in your area.

Expedition Challenge

1. Secure one end of a 50- to 75-cm piece of string to the table top edge with duct tape so the string hangs freely. Make sure the string is very secure and will not come loose when tugged.

2. Make a mark on the string near where it is secured to the table. This will be the zero length mark on your measuring tool.

3. With the string freely and loosely hanging down (straighten it just to make it taut, but do not pull on it), measure 30 cm down the string and mark it with your marker. This length measurement will be called 30 cm at zero tension.

4. Tie the loose end of the string onto the hook of a spring scale or a 1,000 g mass.

5. Apply tension by pulling on the other end of the spring scale until it reads 1,000 g, or by allowing the 1,000 g mass to hang down and pull on the string.

6. Using a meter stick, measure 30 cm from the zero length mark on your string and make a mark. This measurement and tension will represent the standard for this experiment.

7. Record the length at the following tensions (expressed as a function of mass):
   a. 250 g
   b. 500 g
   c. 750 g
   d. 1,250 g
   e. 1,500 g
   f. 1,750 g

8. Graph your data, with tension on the x-axis and length on the y-axis. Plot your points and add a line of best fit for these data.

9. Describe the effect of tension on the length measurement between the two points.

10. Using the graph, determine the measured length under the following tensions (expressed as a function of mass):
    a. 350 g
    b. 1,650 g

Expedition Debrief

1. How did changes in tension affect your measurements?

2. What impact could changes in tension have in the real world?

3. What are some factors you need to take into account to make sure your measuring devices are accurate?

Extension

Experiment with different types of string to determine if they react the same under a variety of tensions.

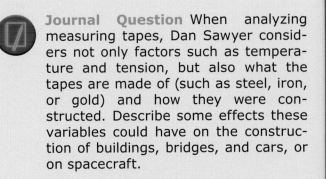

Journal Question When analyzing measuring tapes, Dan Sawyer considers not only factors such as temperature and tension, but also what the tapes are made of (such as steel, iron, or gold) and how they were constructed. Describe some effects these variables could have on the construction of buildings, bridges, and cars, or on spacecraft.

Underwater Cables

Imagine yourself sending a text message to a pen pal on the other side of the Atlantic Ocean:

"How R U?"

A text message like this would take only a matter of moments to compose, send, and receive. Now go back in time about 200 years, and a message like this would require several weeks to send overseas. The six characters in the message above could potentially change hands several times, going from messengers on horseback, to ship ports, to ships, out to sea, back to ship ports, and then on horseback before reaching their final destination. By today's standards, this form of communication would take way too much time and money.

Sounding the Ocean

Soundings of ocean depth have been taken since at least the time of the Vikings. Early soundings were performed by lowering a weight attached to a rope over the side of the ship until it touched bottom. The rope was marked in fathoms, a unit measured as the distance between a sailor's outstretched arms. Later, fathoms were standardized to equal 1.83 meters. However, until the 1840s, there was little interest in sounding the deep sea, once ships had cleared shallower waters around land.

In 1843, Sir James Clark Ross took the first modern, deepsea soundings. One of these soundings didn't reach bottom after 4,000 fathoms, which was the deepest water depth recorded at that time.

softeis/Wikimedia Commons

pd/Wikimedia Commons

US Navy/Wikimedia Commons

However, this was the norm until the 1830s when Professor Samuel Morse, inventor of the Morse code, changed everything. By the use of different "on" and "off" tones Morse created a new form of communication which could be transmitted through telegraph lines. This caused quite a stir as messages could now be sent and received almost instantaneously. Before long, telegraph lines were built on land throughout Europe and North America, revolutionizing communication.

However, it still took weeks for messages to cross the ocean as telegraph lines could not span the entire Atlantic. The size of the Atlantic Ocean posed a great problem. Linking Europe with North America would require thousands of meters of telegraph cable—and not with just any ordinary cable. During a time when wire insulation material was just beginning to be researched, this was quite a large feat. Compared to communication cables over land, underwater cables designed to cross the Atlantic would need to be extremely strong and insulated to withstand erosion caused by salt water. Strength was particularly important as it would be almost impossible to have a repairman come out and fix a broken cable submerged under thousands of meters of water.

Understanding the depth of the water in the Atlantic Ocean was another key factor in being able to lay cable from North America to Europe. There was little understanding of the deep ocean at that time. Some leading theories stated that ships that sank in deep water would never reach the bottom, but would instead be suspended when they reached equilibrium at a certain depth. Many thought that the Atlantic cable would also hang suspended in the water, rather than lie on the bottom of the ocean.

Others, however, believed that the bottom of the deepest ocean could be reached and therefore measured. Throughout the 1840s and 1850s, naval Superintendent of the Depot of Charts and Instruments Matthew Maury, led a charge to gather information about the ocean depths. He equipped all navy ships with simple sounding devices and tasked them with taking soundings as they sailed. This differed greatly from the previous practice of concentrating research activities to research vessels. Plans for laying the Atlantic cable helped intensify efforts to sound and map the Atlantic, and the U.S. navy played a large role in charting the ocean depths.

Production of the first transatlantic cable began in early 1857. Several months later, close to 3,000 miles of cable made from 340,000 miles of intertwined copper wiring encased in about 300 tons of insulation was ready for the journey. The finished cable was so massive that it took two ships, the *U.S.S. Niagara* and the *H.M.S. Agamemnon*, to carry everything.

The ships and crew started off on their journey and sailed from Valentia Bay, Ireland, and headed for Trinity Bay, Newfoundland. Unfortunately, after only about a short distance out into sea, the cable snapped. After another botched attempt just under a year later, on August 4 1858, the *U.S.S. Niagara* reached its destination in Trinity Bay. The two continents were connected for the first time via the transatlantic! The first official telegram, a letter of congratulations, was sent from Queen Victoria to James Buchanan, the President of the United States. Maury's information about the deep ocean floor was credited as essential to the success.

Gregory Moine/flickr

matthew brady/Wikimedia Commons

"Maury furnished the brains, England gave the money, and I did the work."

– Cyrus West Field, leader of the Atlantic cable efforts at dinner celebrating the first transatlantic message.

pd/Wikimedia Commons

However, disaster struck again as a few weeks later, the link was broken. The cause of this break was possibly a voltage overload. It was not until July of 1866 when a second, much improved, transatlantic cable was successfully laid. This one has stood the test of time. Today, thousands of kilometers of underwater cables are strewn throughout our oceans connecting countries all over the world.

Your Turn

The "on" and "off" tapping sounds of Morse code compared to email and text messaging seems very inefficient these days. But if you go back less than a few hundred years, this was the way long distance communication was done. Using a Morse code chart, create a message to send to a friend across the room.

"I feel like I am saving lives. I have the ability to see the research that I've done be incorporated into how vehicles are redesigned, and to see the improvements that have been made. And as a result, the risk of death in certain kinds of crashes has decreased."

—Matt Brumbelow
Senior Research Engineer, IIHS

Matt Brumbelow

At the Insurance Institute for Highway Safety (IIHS), Matt Brumbelow uses crash test dummies—and his knowledge of forces and motion—to understand what happens to passengers in car crashes. Matt's work helps save lives by making cars safer.

Meet the Researcher Video
Join Matt behind the scenes of a car crash and explore how his creative applications of the laws of physics help save lives in car crashes.

Senior Research Engineer, IIHS   INSURANCE INSTITUTE FOR HIGHWAY SAFETY

Read more about Matt online in the JASON Expedition Center.

Peter Haydock/The JASON Project

Photo Credits (left to right): vmiramontes/flickr; M.Minderhoud/Wikimedia Commons; Morven/Wikimedia Commons; NASA; Peter Haydock/The JASON Project; Fir0002/Wikimedia Commons

Your Expedition Goal...

Investigate and analyze the factors that describe motion and position.

To accomplish your expedition goal successfully, you will need to

- Discover how motion is relative to a standard reference point.
- Distinguish between scalar and vector quantities of motion.
- Explore the motion of an object by describing its position, direction, and speed.
- Create and interpret a variety of motion graphs.
- Discover how distance/displacement, speed/velocity, acceleration, and momentum are all connected by the rate of change.
- Apply the Law of Conservation of Momentum to analyze crash tests performed at the Insurance Institute for Highway Safety (IIHS).

Join the Team

After having crashed a car into a truck trailer at the Insurance Institute for Highway Safety (IIHS), the Argonauts with Matt Brumbelow examine the car and the trailer to determine if a person would survive in a collision like this. Back Row (L to R): Martin Kelsey, Matt Brumbelow, Maggy Botros, Sarah Mullins, Melinda Woods-Carpenter, Lisa Conselatore, and Kendra Elie. Front Row (L to R): Kate Burnett, Kelly Stewart, Karthik Uppaluri, Keiana Yasunaka, Dean Taylor, Marcelo Ancira, and Aubrey Gonzalez.

Bill Jewell/The JASON Project

Peter Haydock/The JASON Project

Crash Course in Safety

In a large hangar, a voice over the loud speaker calls out, "Test to begin in 20 seconds." Soon, a large door lifts up and you hear the roar of a motor as a car carrying a crash test dummy accelerates down a long, narrow runway. As it approaches the center of the room, you see the large 18-wheel truck it is about to slam into, and then. . . there is a deafening crash as glass and metal shoots across the room. Almost immediately, a team of scientists and engineers with clipboards descend upon the scene to assess the damage.

We all need to get on the road to travel every day, so it's easy to forget that traveling is—and has always been—inherently dangerous. Almost six million car crashes are reported to U.S. police annually, and many more go unreported. Each year in the U.S., about 37,000 people die from those accidents. Although it is sad to think about the people who are killed, it is encouraging to know that our cars have gotten increasingly safer over the years.

Amazing scientists and engineers, like Matt Brumbelow and his colleagues at the Insurance Institute for Highway Safety (IIHS), work to prevent injuries and loss of life in car accidents. Matt Brumbelow performs a variety of crash tests with many makes and models of cars. On the front line of protecting drivers and passengers are crash test dummies, which are custom built to simulate the human body and collect data before, during, and after the crashes. Matt uses his understanding of concepts like velocity, acceleration, and momentum to advise car insurers, manufacturers, and consumers about the safety of today's automobiles.

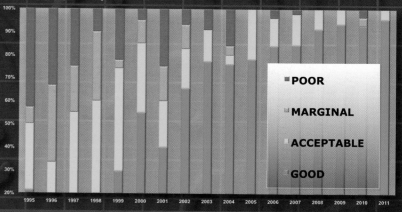

▼ The number of cars that obtain a "good" rating (in green) from IIHS for safety in frontal crash tests has increased in recent years, while the number of cars that obtain "poor" ratings (in red) has decreased.

POOR

MARGINAL

ACCEPTABLE

GOOD

Expedition 2 Briefing

Video Prepare for your expedition by viewing this briefing on your objectives. Learn how Matt Brumbelow and his team apply the physics of forces and motion to better understand what happens in car crashes.

In This Stage:

Your expedition goal is accomplished when you:

Can determine whether an object is in motion or not.

Know what scalar and vector quantities are and how are they different.

Why this is important:

Everything in the universe is in motion relative to something. Motion is fundamental to just about anything scientists and engineers do.

Words to Identify

reference point, motion, distance, scalar, displacement, vector, vector arrows, rate, speed, instantaneous speed, constant speed, average speed, velocity

Expedition Briefing

Stage 1: On the Move

Talking About Motion

As engineers such as Matt Brumbelow investigate how to make transportation safer, they need to understand what makes crashes dangerous in the first place. Understanding how a car crash at 40 kph (25 mph) compares to a crash at 55 kph (34 mph) might sound like a small difference. But, as Matt is learning, it could mean the difference between life and death. To begin answering questions like these, we have to start at the very beginning: how do we know something is moving in the first place?

Peter Haydock/The JASON Pro

Try This!

Using resources approved by your teacher, research some of the cars that would have been on the roads when IIHS first started their work in 1959. Document how their shapes and bumpers are different from what we see on the road today. Why do you think they have changed?

Morven/Wikimedia Commons

Reference Point

Imagine you and a friend are sitting together as you ride on a bus. Would you say your friend is moving or not moving? What about a person standing on the sidewalk as you ride by? If you read the words on this page while sitting in a chair at school, would you say the words are moving? It all depends on your reference point.

A **reference point** is the location from which motion is studied. And depending on your reference point, your observations of something could change. For example, if the reference point is the person standing on the sidewalk, then the bus and all its passengers would appear to be in motion. However, if the reference point is someone on the bus, the other passengers are not in motion, but the person standing on the sidewalk is in motion. **Motion** is any change in the position of an object relative to a reference point.

So the words on this page might or might not be in motion depending on your reference point. If your reference point is the chair you are sitting in, then the words on this page are not in motion. However, if your reference point is the planet Jupiter, then these words would really be moving.

Distance—A Scalar Quantity

Once an object is determined to be in motion, the next step would be to measure how much the object has moved. Motion can be measured in two ways, **distance** and **displacement**.

In Expedition 1, we discussed how the meter base unit is used to measure length or distance. But, what is distance? **Distance** measures how far apart two objects are from one another. It can refer to the few millimeters the steering wheel can press into a crash test dummy's chest, or it can refer to the millions of kilometers between Earth and Mars. Distance is a scalar quantity.

Scalar quantities are those that only have magnitude. For example, if a friend told you that she walked a distance of one kilometer, you would only know how far she walked (the magnitude), not in which direction she walked. Distance is a scalar quantity because it only describes the magnitude, or amount of a measurement. Unlike scalar quantities, some measurements have two characteristics: magnitude and direction. These are called **vector** quantities.

A **scalar quantity has one characteristic: magnitude.** Distance and speed are examples of scalar quantities.

A **vector quantity has two characteristics: magnitude and direction.** Displacement and velocity are examples of vector quantities.

▼ The high speed cameras used at IIHS can capture incredible images because they can take pictures at rates up to 1,000 frames per second!

IIHS

Displacement—A Vector Quantity

Displacement measures the numerical difference between the end (final) position and start (initial) position of an object, as well as the direction that the object traveled. It is a vector quantity because it has two characteristics: magnitude and direction. Therefore, to describe displacement, you must know the distance between your final position and your initial position, as well as the direction of your final position relative to your initial position.

For example, suppose a car starts at school, drives 6 km west to a library, and then travels 10 km northeast to get home. The total distance the car travels is 16 km (6 km to the library plus 10 km to get home). By including the direction the car traveled, a more complete picture of the trip can be determined, and displacement can be calculated. In this case, the car traveled west 6 km to the library and then northeast 10 km to return home. Although it traveled a distance of 16 km, the car's overall displacement, or change in position from its initial position, is 8 km north.

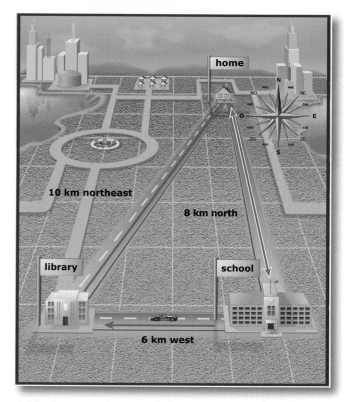

▲ The car travels a total distance of 16 kilometers to get home from school. However, once home, its displacement from the school is only 8 kilometers north.

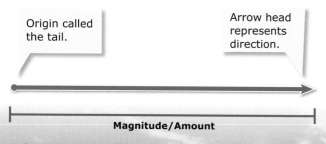

▲ A vector arrow (blue arrow) represents magnitude (red bracket) and direction.

Try This!

Measure and mark 10–meter, 15–meter, and 20–meter distances. Have a classmate time how long it takes you to hop 10 meters, skip 15 meters, and run 20 meters. Calculate the speed for each method (Speed = distance / time). Compare the three speeds. Which was the fastest method? The slowest?

Vector Arrows

Because displacement includes both distance and direction, vector arrows are often used to help visualize displacement. **Vector arrows** are arrows that represent both the magnitude and the direction of motion. A vector arrow has a tail and a head. The magnitude is represented by the length between the tail and the head. A scale, such as 1 cm = 20 km, is often used to convey the actual distance between the two points. The arrow's direction represents the direction of the displacement vector.

Since each vector arrow represents a specific direction, changes in direction are shown with a new vector arrow. These arrows can be placed head to tail to describe the motion. The distance and direction from the tail of the first vector (the origin) to the head of the last vector is the displacement.

sumbrze2010/flickr

das farbamt/flickr

versageek/flickr

Adding and Subtracting Vector Arrows

Adding and subtracting vector quantities differs from adding and subtracting scalar quantities because the direction is included in the vector calculations. For example, suppose a bird flew 40 kilometers east and then turned around and flew 20 kilometers west. The displacement of the bird from the starting point would be 20 kilometers to the east. The distance the bird flew was 60 kilometers.

For Matt Brumbelow, understanding the difference between distance and displacement is crucial. For example, when he analyzes a crash test dummy's head after a collision, it may not appear to have moved much, and the overall displacement might be very small. However, during a crash, the dummy's head may have moved a great distance—forward, backward, or side to side. For a human, this movement could cause serious damage. Matt has to be able to distinguish between distance traveled and displacement in order to provide accurate reports about a car's safety.

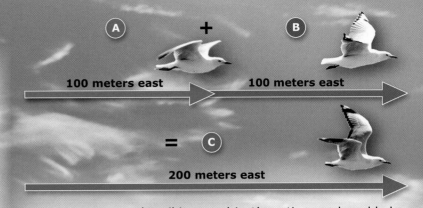

▲ Vector arrows describing an object's motion can be added together to determine overall displacement. In this example, the bird travels 100 meters east (A) and then another 100 meters east (B) for a total displacement of 200 meters east (C).

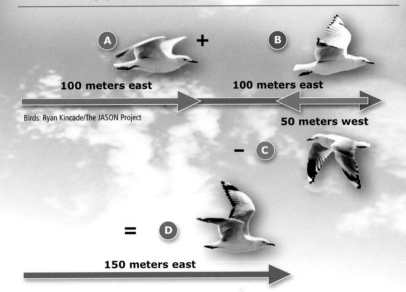

Birds: Ryan Kincade/The JASON Project

▲ When a vector indicates a direction opposite of the initial direction, that vector is considered negative. The bird travels 200 meters east (A and B), before traveling 50 meters west (C). The total displacement of the bird was 150 meters east (D).

Rates of Change

In Expedition 1, we explored time and how it is used to measure the interval between events using hours, minutes, and seconds. Time can also be used to help describe rate. **Rate** is the amount of change in any measurement over time. For example, if you did ten jumping jacks in one minute, your rate of jumping jacks would be 10 jumping jacks per minute. If you scored three goals in a one-hour soccer match, your rate of goal-scoring would be 3 goals per hour.

Measuring rate helps us to monitor change. For example, at rest, your heart may beat at a rate of 60 beats per minute. Try monitoring your heart rate as you exercise. You will definitely notice an increase in heart rate.

One of the easiest things to observe in the world is change. If you compare a picture of yourself as a baby to a picture of yourself from this year, you will notice you have changed. If the soda machine charges $0.50 one day and $0.75 the next day, you will notice the change. In order to react to these observations, you will need to consider the rate at which these changes happen.

Check for Understanding

✓ How are vector arrows used to describe motion?

✓ Why is it important to understand rates of change?

One rate you are probably familiar with is speed. **Speed** is the distance traveled over a given period of time. For example, on many U.S. interstate highways, the speed limit that cars can travel is 97 kilometers per hour (60 miles per hour). That means that in one hour, cars traveling at that speed will have traveled a distance of 97 kilometers (about 60 miles).

Calculating speed allows us to compare moving objects even if they are not traveling together. For example, it is easy to tell which car is fastest in a race, but how easy would it be to determine whether tennis players can serve the ball faster than a peregrine falcon can dive through the air? Calculating speed makes this comparison easy. While some tennis players can serve the ball at speeds upwards of 200 kph (124 mph), it is still far slower than a peregrine falcon, which can dive to attack prey at speeds up to 320 kph (198.8 mph).

At IIHS, Matt Brumbelow and his team study cars moving at different speeds in order to determine how effectively cars protect passengers. By studying crashes from speeds as low as 32 kph (20 mph) to speeds of 64 kph (40 mph) and higher, Matt and his team can examine how well a car model protects its passengers in different situations.

Types of Speed

Speed is defined as the change in distance over time, but there are different ways to examine an object's speed. Depending upon how the speed is being determined, the speed can be instantaneous, constant, or average. Therefore, when the speed of a car or other object is described, the type of speed should be identified as well.

To understand the differences among these three types of speed, imagine that a race car is being driven around a racetrack. At any time, the driver can look at the speedometer on the car's dashboard. The speedometer provides a measurement of the car's instantaneous speed. **Instantaneous speed** is the speed of an object at an exact moment in time. If the car were to stop at a pit stop, its instantaneous speed would be zero.

If the car could to travel around the racetrack without its speed changing over time, then the car would be moving at a **constant speed**. For example, if the car drives at 60 kph, then after one hour, it will have traveled exactly 60 kilometers.

simongreenuk/flickr

Calculating Speed

Speed is equal to distance divided by time. With that in mind, can you answer the following?

A cheetah ran 40 meters in two seconds. How fast did it run?

speed = 40 m / 2 s

The cheetah's speed was 20 m/s.

A car drove 120 kilometers in 2 hours. How fast did it drive?

speed = 120 km / 2 hours

The car's speed was 60 km/h.

The distance traveled over a period of time (m/s or km/h).

speed = distance / time

How far an object moved (m or km).

How long an object moved (s or h).

Unless the car and cheetah went that fast the entire time they were in motion—from the moment they started, until the moment they finished—the speeds you calculated were the average speeds. Average speed takes into account that the car and the cheetah went faster at some points and slower at others during their trips.

Most moving objects do not move at a constant speed. For example, as a car travels around a racetrack, it slows down for curves and speeds up as the course straightens out. Because the speed of the car varies throughout a lap, the **average speed** should be used to describe the speed of the car as it completes a lap. To figure out the average speed, you need to know the total distance the car traveled and the time it took to travel that distance.

Graphing Speed

Scientists and engineers such as Matt Brumbelow have found that graphs are a particularly useful tool for studying speed and motion. Speed is distance over time; therefore, graphs of the distance over time allow them to visualize the speed of an object. For example, suppose a car races through the twists and turns of a 450-meter racetrack in 20 seconds. During the course, the car speeds up, slows down, and even stops at times. The car's motion can be graphed for examination.

When graphing speed, the time is plotted on the x-axis and the distance is plotted on the y-axis. The slope of the line created indicates what the object, in this case the car, is doing. Each segment of the graph describes the speed the car was traveling at that moment.

Slope is the steepness of the line on a graph. Slope indicates how fast a variable, such as distance, changes in relation to another variable, such as time. To calculate slope between two points, divide the rise (the vertical difference between two points) by the run (the horizontal difference between the same two points).

$$slope = rise/run$$

The slope of a line on a graph of distance vs. time can indicate how fast a car is going.

Fast Fact

For something made to be damaged, crash test dummies sure are expensive! The crash dummies IIHS uses cost from $60,000 to $200,000 each. The price depends upon which sensors and computers Matt Brumbelow and other engineers need in order to thoroughly study car crashes. While the dummy body is reusable, many parts can be damaged in the crash tests, and if so, must be replaced.

Brady Holt/Wikimedia Commons

Distance vs. Time

Goal = 50 m

Time (s)

These graphs indicate two cars racing—one traveling 18 m/s (blue line) and the other traveling 9 m/s (red line). The car traveling the blue line would win the race because it reaches the goal distance of 50 m first.

Measuring Speed

Examine the distance versus time graph on this page of a car traveling around town. You will note points when the car was traveling at a constant speed, going faster, slowing down, and not moving at all.

1. Before the car starts moving, it has traveled zero meters, and time has not started.
2. The car has started moving, and the slope of the graph starts increasing.
3. The car has slowed down. Because it is taking longer for the car to travel each meter, the slope slightly decreases. Notice, however, although the slope decreases, it is not horizontal. This is because the car is still moving.
4. The car has started going faster, and the slope increases again.
5. The car stops at a traffic light. The slope is zero and the line is horizontal. Time is passing, but the car does not travel any distance.
6. The car starts moving again, so the slope of the line increases.

Distance vs. Time

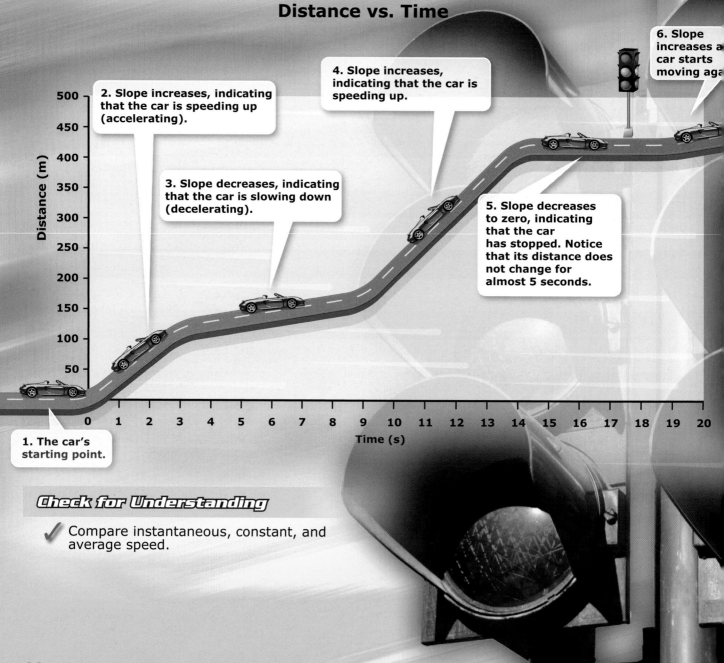

2. Slope increases, indicating that the car is speeding up (accelerating).

4. Slope increases, indicating that the car is speeding up.

6. Slope increases a car starts moving aga

3. Slope decreases, indicating that the car is slowing down (decelerating).

5. Slope decreases to zero, indicating that the car has stopped. Notice that its distance does not change for almost 5 seconds.

1. The car's starting point.

Check for Understanding

✓ Compare instantaneous, constant, and average speed.

horiavlan/flickr

Velocity - A Vector Quantity

Speed is an example of a scalar quantity. It only shows "how fast" the car is traveling, and does not show in which direction the car is traveling.

The use of speed as a measure has its limits during Matt Brumbelow's testing. Cars respond to crashes differently depending on the direction from which they are hit. So Matt needs to know both the magnitude and the direction in which cars are traveling. He does this using velocity. **Velocity** is a vector quantity which represents both the speed and the direction in which an object is moving. For example, a car can be described as traveling at a speed of 60 kph. If the car is traveling north, its velocity is 60 kph north.

Our Ocean Planet

They may not be able to run fast, but some of the speediest creatures on Earth can be found in the ocean. The fastest known fish is the sailfish, which has been documented at speeds up to 109 kph (67.7 mph)—just a little less than a cheetah's top speed of about 112 kph (69.5 mph), though nowhere near the peregrine falcon's top speed of 320 kph (198.8 mph). Tuna, a favorite seafood, has recorded speeds of up to 74 kph (46 kph).

Ocean mammals are pretty fast, too. Killer whales, the largest of the dolphins, are speedy predators that can swim at 56 kph (34.7 mph). Blue whales, the largest animals known to have lived on Earth, can move their massive bodies through the water at up 32 kph (19.8 mph). Believe it or not, the fearsome great white shark of *Jaws* fame clocks in at only about 24 kph (14.9 mph)—the equivalent of an elephant's fastest recorded land speed.

The distinction between speed and velocity is important because direction can be critical in some cases. For instance, it is not enough for air traffic controllers to know the speed of incoming planes. They must also know the direction in which the planes are flying. Knowing the velocity of the planes allows them to prevent possible collisions.

Direction is also important to engineers at IIHS during crash tests. A car that Matt Brumbelow tests might perform very well during rear impact collisions, but might not do as well in side impact tests. Matt and the engineers at IIHS need to calculate the velocity of the car as well as the velocity of the moving crash test dummies. The directions in which the car and the dummies move are critical to IIHS's quest to protect property and save lives.

Check for Understanding

✓ What are some instances in which it is important to know the velocity, rather than the speed, of an object?

✓ Compare speed and velocity.

Calculating Velocity

A dolphin swimming alongside a ship traveled 12 meters directly north in 3 seconds. What was its velocity?

velocity = 12 m north / 3 s

The dolphin's velocity was 4 m/s north.

A car drove 80 kilometers west in 2 hours. What was its velocity?

velocity = 80 km west / 2 h

The car's velocity was 40 km/h west.

The average distance an object traveled in one direction during a period of time (m/s or km/h and a direction).

velocity = displacement / time

The distance and direction an object moved (m or km, and a direction).

The total time during which the object moved (s or h).

Graphing Velocity

To describe the velocity of an object, the displacement of the object is needed. Displacement describes both distance and direction from the initial position to the final position. The time during which the object was displaced is also needed.

Velocity can be calculated by dividing the displacement of an object from its initial position by the time during which the object was displaced to its final position.

This graph shows the velocity of a bus during a trip. Velocity is a vector quantity, so the graph shows displacement (distance and direction from the initial position) compared to time. As the bus travels away from its initial position in a straight line, its velocity is positive since its displacement is increasing. This is shown on the graph by a rising, or positive, slope. When the bus turns around and travels back toward its initial position, its displacement is decreasing and so its velocity is negative. This is shown on the graph by a falling, or negative, slope.

Team Highlight

Argonauts (L to R): Maggy Botros, Lisa Conselatore, Kendra Elie, and Kate Burnett study a device used to calibrate crash dummies at IIHS. By dropping the mass from the same height, sensors in the dummies are adjusted, ensuring that the data from each collision are comparable.

Peter Haydock/The JASON Project

Displacement vs. Time

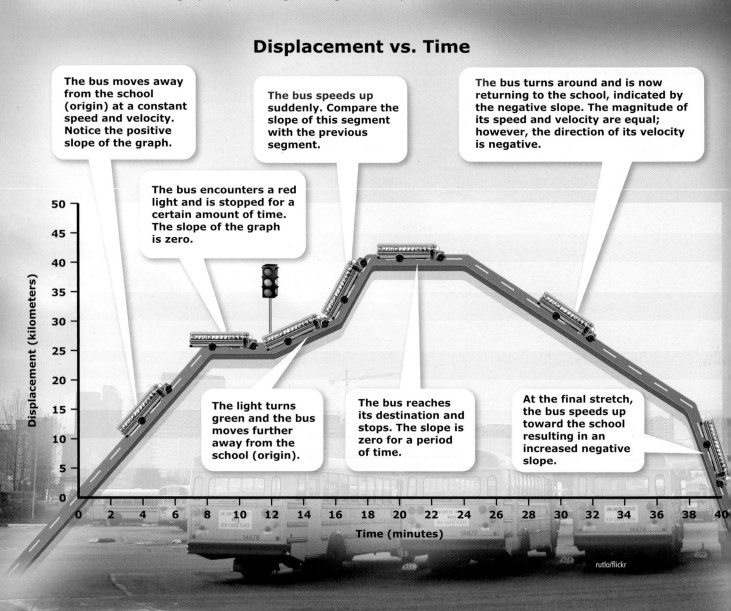

The bus moves away from the school (origin) at a constant speed and velocity. Notice the positive slope of the graph.

The bus encounters a red light and is stopped for a certain amount of time. The slope of the graph is zero.

The bus speeds up suddenly. Compare the slope of this segment with the previous segment.

The bus turns around and is now returning to the school, indicated by the negative slope. The magnitude of its speed and velocity are equal; however, the direction of its velocity is negative.

The light turns green and the bus moves further away from the school (origin).

The bus reaches its destination and stops. The slope is zero for a period of time.

At the final stretch, the bus speeds up toward the school resulting in an increased negative slope.

rutlo/flickr

Calculating Speed and Determining Velocity

When Matt Brumbelow and his team at the Insurance Institute for Highway Safety test cars to determine their safety in a collision, they consider speed and velocity. The speed of a car in a collision can greatly affect the outcome of the collision. In 2009, speeding was a factor in 31 percent of all vehicle crash deaths.

In this activity, you will create a track for a ball to roll along. Using this track, you will calculate the speed of several balls of different sizes and masses. You will explore how various factors affect an object's speed and how an object's speed affects its velocity in an impact.

Materials
- Lab 1 Data Sheet
- 2-4, 4-meter pieces of pipe insulation with at least a 1" diameter opening, cut in half lengthwise
- toothpicks
- 3 or 4 balls/marbles of different sizes and masses
- tape measure/ruler/meter stick
- stopwatch
- balance/scale
- tape
- string
- assortment of materials to elevate track, such as cups or books

Lab Prep

1. Attach two to four pieces of foam pipe insulation together, using toothpicks to make one long piece. Measure and record the total length of the piece.

2. Use the foam to set up a track for balls to race down. Use materials such as books or cups to create hills in the track. Place a sturdy barrier at the end of the track for the balls to crash into.

3. Test the track with each of the balls to make sure they will make it to the end. Adjust the track as needed.

4. Use a scale or balance to measure the mass of each ball. Record the mass and a description of each ball, including texture and type of material.

5. Stretch a piece of string from the start of the track directly to the barrier at end of the track. Measure the length of the string to determine the magnitude of the displacement from the beginning of the track to the barrier.

Make Observations

1. Release each ball one at a time down the track.

2. Using the stopwatch, time how long it takes for each ball to reach the end of the track. Repeat this process two more times for each ball.

3. Determine the average time for each ball from the three trials.

4. Make observations about each ball's motion after it strikes the barrier at the end of the track. Does it just stop? Does it bounce back? If the balls bounce back, do they all bounce back the same distance and speed?

5. Determine the average speed of each ball using the formula:
   speed = distance / time

6. Graph your data. Put time on the x-axis and distance on the y-axis. Plot the average speed of each ball as a point. Then draw a line from each point to (0,0) in the bottom left corner of the graph.

Reflect and Apply

1. What variables might cause the balls to travel at different speeds?

2. Develop a hypothesis about which variables may be causing differences in the balls' motion after they strike the barrier.

Extension

Keeping either the distance or displacement the same, create a different track design and test the speed of each ball on the new track.

 Journal Question Why do the balls react differently when they strike the barrier at the end of the track?

In This Stage:

Your expedition goal is accomplished when you:

Know how to calculate and graph acceleration.

Understand non-linear motion.

Why this is important:

Few things in the universe move at a constant velocity. To truly understand motion, you have to understand changing velocities.

Words to Identify

acceleration, decelerate, linear motion, non-linear motion, projectile motion, projectile, trajectory, circular motion

Stage 2: Speeding Up, Slowing Down, and Spinning Around

Acceleration

In the real world, a constant velocity is rare. Whether it is a cheetah running through a field after an antelope or a truck being tested at Matt Brumbelow's lab, objects change their velocity by speeding up, slowing down, stopping, and changing direction. **Acceleration** is the rate at which velocity changes. Acceleration describes these changes in speed and direction.

Suppose you are in a car stopped at a red light. When the light changes and the car moves forward, it begins to go faster. You and the car accelerate. When the velocity of a moving object increases, the object accelerates. If the car slows down for another red light, the car is accelerating, although it is a negative acceleration. When the velocity of a moving object decreases, it is said to **decelerate**, or undergo negative acceleration.

Even an object traveling at a constant speed can accelerate. Because acceleration describes the rate at which velocity changes, and velocity has both a magnitude (speed) and direction, acceleration must consider both. Therefore, acceleration describes changes in direction as well as those in speed. For example, if the car you are in turns left at an intersection, the car is accelerating, even if it doesn't slow down or speed up.

During crash tests at IIHS, the cars that are tested accelerate and decelerate. All the cars begin their crash test from a stationary position. Their starting acceleration is zero. The cars are then accelerated to the appropriate testing speed by a computer program. Deceleration occurs upon impact.

▼ Both cars shown below are accelerating. Because the first car is speeding up while moving forward, the acceleration is positive. The second car is slowing down. It is still accelerating, but because it is slowing down, the acceleration is negative.

Velocity vs. Time

The red line shows positive acceleration, or velocity of an object increasing over time.

The blue line shows negative acceleration, or the velocity of an object decreasing over time.

The yellow line shows that the object is not accelerating, or the velocity is staying the same over time.

(Velocity (m/s) axis: 0, 5, 10, 15, 20, 25, 30, 35, 40, 45, 50, 55, 60, 65, 70; Time (s) axis: 0 1 2 3 4 5 6 7 8 9 10 11 12 13 14 15 16 17 18 19 20)

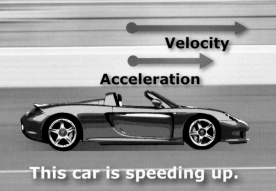

Velocity

Acceleration

This car is speeding up.

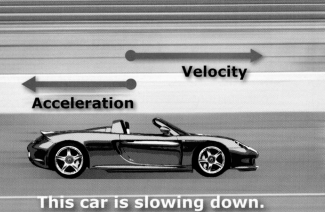

Velocity

Acceleration

This car is slowing down.

Calculating Acceleration

As she approached the finish line, a racer running east accelerated from 8 meters per second to 10 meters per second during the last second of the race. What was her rate of acceleration?

acceleration =

(10 m/s east − 8 m/s east) / 1 s = 2 m/s² east

The runner accelerated at a rate of 2 m/s² east.

The change in velocity over a period of time (m/s² or km/h²).

acceleration = change in velocity / time

Final velocity of an object − initial velocity (m/s or km/h).

Time during which the object moved (s or h).

Graphing Acceleration

Graphs that illustrate an object's acceleration are different from graphs that illustrate velocity. Velocity is the rate of change of displacement. Acceleration measures the rate of change of velocity.

When graphing the acceleration of an object, the time during which it moved is plotted horizontally on the x-axis. Its velocity is plotted vertically on the y-axis. The slope of the line illustrates whether the object is speeding up or slowing down.

An object that is speeding up will have an upward (positive) slope. An object that is slowing down will have a downward (negative) slope. An object that is traveling at a constant velocity, neither slowing down nor speeding up, is represented on the graph by a straight horizontal line (no slope).

Acceleration as a Vector

Acceleration is the change in velocity, which is a vector quantity. Even if a car moves at a constant speed around a turn, the velocity changes because the direction changes. If velocity is changing, then the car is accelerating.

For example, consider a rider on a merry-go-round. The rider is moving at a constant speed, but the direction is always changing as he or she moves in circles. The velocity is changing, so the rider on the merry-go-round is accelerating. However, objects moving in a circular path act differently than those moving in straight lines, and are approached differently.

Check for Understanding

✓ How can an object be moving at a constant speed yet still be accelerating?

This car is turning with a constant speed.

Velocity

Acceleration

Non-Linear Motion

So far we have explored **linear motion**, or motion in a line or in one dimension. One–dimensional motion occurs when velocity, acceleration, and displacement all occur along one direction, forward and backward. However, motion does not always occur in one dimension. For example, during IIHS crash tests, motion is not limited to a straight line, as crashed cars can move to the left or right, as well as move up and down after impact. In fact, Matt Brumbelow cannot get a full safety picture without considering what happens when cars turn corners, travel up and down hills, and move sideways to change lanes. If Matt examined cars moving only in one dimension, a lot of lifesaving data would be missing.

In order to examine these changes in motion, Matt Brumbelow needs to understand non-linear motion. In **non-linear motion**, velocity, acceleration, and displacement do not all occur in a straight line. Instead, the motion of an object as well as its acceleration and velocity, occurs in more than one direction. Non-linear motion can be either circular or projectile motion.

Projectile Motion

If you have ever made a shot with a basketball, you may have noticed that the ball moves forward in the direction it was thrown, as well as up toward the basket. But as gravity acts upon it, the ball also starts moving down toward Earth. This upward and forward path is known as **projectile motion**. Any object dropped, tossed vertically, or launched horizontally on Earth, and influenced by the original external force and acted on only by the force of gravity is known as a **projectile**.

Gravity is the force of attraction that exists between two objects. On Earth, gravity causes objects to fall toward the ground because Earth is so massive.

Force is anything, such as a push or a pull, that causes a change in the motion of a freely movable object, or that causes stress in a fixed object.

Inertia is an object's resistance to change in its state of motion. An object in motion will remain in motion and an object at rest will remain at rest until acted upon by an outside force.

In projectile motion, assuming no air resistance, once an object is in motion, the force of gravity acts upon that object. Therefore, the object experiences acceleration due to gravity in the vertically downward direction. A projectile's motion will be the resultant of two vectors—horizontal and vertical. There is no horizontal acceleration, so the horizontal velocity is constant.

The vertical vector represents the force of gravity on the object in a downward direction. Since on Earth, at sea level, gravity is a constant 9.8 m/s^2, the object will accelerate downward at this rate. A projectile's horizontal vector is independent of its vertical vector. Since these two vectors act independently from each other, they produce the projectile's characteristic arc-shaped path called a **trajectory**.

Now that you know exactly what is happening, you can apply your understanding to a variety of games and situations—like throwing darts, hitting a baseball, shooting an arrow, or tossing a ball to your dog.

minghong/flickr

Team Highlight

Dean Taylor, Melinda Woods-Carpenter, and Maggy Botros examine the different crash dummies used at IIHS. Researchers at IIHS study not only the many types of car collisions, but also child safety seats, car seats, and even bumpers.

Peter Haydock/The JASON Project

A missile shot from a cannon is an example of a projectile. The projectile is shot from the cannon with an initial force, but is then affected only by gravity (assuming there is no air resistance). The horizontal velocity is constant, since no force is acting on it horizontally. The horizontal motion is due to inertia, so it will continue horizontally at the same speed and direction that the initial force from the cannon sent it.

Acceleration due to gravity is a constant on Earth: 9.8 m/s^2. All projectiles fall at this rate. So a cannonball shot straight ahead from a cannon and one simply dropped from the exact same height will reach the ground at the same time.

Several factors can affect the trajectory of a cannonball or any projectile. Cannonballs shot from the same height will reach the ground at the same time. But the initial force with which the cannonball is fired will affect its velocity. Its velocity will affect how far it travels horizontally before it reaches the ground. A cannonball with a greater horizontal velocity will fall to the ground at the same time as one with less initial velocity. But since it is going faster, it will travel further horizontally before it hits the ground.

The angle at which the cannonball is fired from the cannon also affects its trajectory. Remember that after the initial force from the cannon is applied, the cannonball continues to travel at the same speed and in the same direction of that initial force until another force acts on it.

If a cannon fires straight ahead, inertia will keep the cannonball moving straight ahead horizontally. At the same time, gravity will cause it to accelerate vertically until it reaches the ground.

Now imagine the cannon fires the cannonball at an angle. In this case, the cannonball has both horizontal and vertical inertia. The horizontal inertia means the cannonball keeps travelling in a horizontal direction at the same velocity. The vertical inertia keeps the cannonball in the air longer than if it had just been fired straight ahead horizontally. Therefore, a cannonball fired at an angle will be able to travel further than one fired straight ahead because it will be in the air for longer and will have more time to travel horizontally.

◀ Human cannonballs put their lives on the line every time they shoot themselves out of a cannon. If their calculations regarding mass, velocity, and distance are off the slightest bit, they could miss the net and hit the ground. Luckily, math is on their side, and safe landings can happen every time.

75°

60°

45°

30°

15°

Fir0002/Wikimedia Commons

Circular Motion

Suppose an object attached to a rope, like a tetherball, is moving in **circular motion** at a constant speed. The speed of the object is not changing. But because the ball's direction is continually changing, the velocity of the ball is changing too. Remember that acceleration is a change in velocity. In this case, the magnitude of the velocity is not changing, but the direction of the velocity is continually changing, which causes acceleration.

The acceleration of the object moving in a circular path is directed at a right angle to the direction of the object's velocity. This means that if the rope attached to the tetherball were to break, the ball would fly straight ahead rather than continue along the rope's path.

Check for Understanding

✓ Describe two types of non-linear motion.

Scientists use an idea similar to the object on a string to keep satellites in orbit around Earth. Satellites must exactly balance the pull of gravity with the satellite's tendency to keep moving. In the case of a satellite, the force of gravity is similar to the pull of the rope on the tetherball. If the satellite moves too slowly, gravity will pull it back toward Earth. If the satellite moves too quickly, it will fly out of orbit and continue moving in a straight line.

NASA

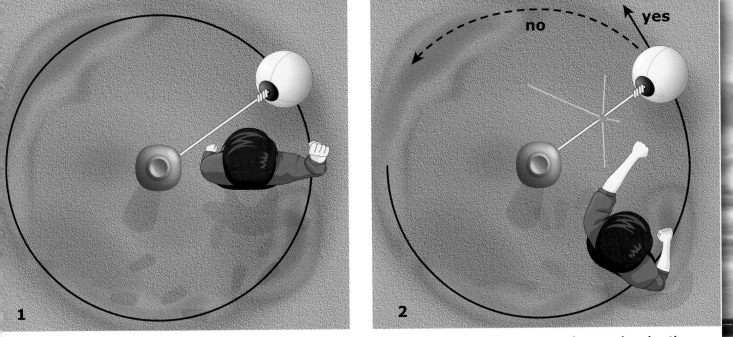

1

2

▲ Although you might think a tetherball would continue traveling in a circle, at the moment the rope breaks, the ball would actually travel in a straight line. This is because the force of the rope would no longer be holding the ball on its path.

alainlm/Wikimedia Commons

Acceleration

Cars rarely travel at a constant velocity. They are often speeding up, slowing down, and changing direction. That is, cars are constantly accelerating. Understanding how acceleration—both positive and negative—affects cars is crucial to Matt Brumbelow and the engineers at IIHS. Therefore, they need to be able to identify changes to a car's acceleration as part of their testing.

In this activity, you will build a tool to detect acceleration. You will use this tool to make observations about changes in speed and direction.

Materials
- Lab 2 Data Sheet
- soda bottle with cap (larger than 8 oz)
- string or thread
- small metal nut
- hot glue
- water
- corn syrup

Lab Prep

1. To build an acceleration detector, first cut the string so that it hangs a bit less than three-quarters of the way down the bottle.

2. Tie the metal nut to the end of the string hanging into the bottle.

3. Attach the other end of the string to the inside center of the bottle's cap using hot glue.

4. Fill the bottle with a mixture of 75 percent corn syrup and 25 percent water that has been shaken well.

5. Screw the cap on the bottle tightly, keeping the metal nut inside the bottle.

Make Observations

1. Push the acceleration detector slowly across the table at a constant speed. Record your observations of the metal nut's movement.

2. Move the acceleration detector across the table and gradually decrease its speed. Record your observations of the metal nut's movement.

3. Move the acceleration detector across the table again, and gradually increase its speed. Again record your observations.

4. Move the acceleration detector across the table at a constant speed, and then change its direction. What happened to the metal nut? Record your observations.

5. Walk around the room holding the acceleration detector in a vertical position. Make other changes in motion (e.g., stopping, changing direction). In each case, record the motion you made and your observations of the metal nut's movement.

Reflect and Apply

1. What types of motion cause the position of the metal nut to change in the acceleration detector?

2. What variables affect how far the metal nut moves?

Extension

1. Attach the acceleration detector to a large toy car or truck. Roll the toy car down a ramp or across the floor and observe the motion of the metal nut. Record your observations.

2. Bring your acceleration detector on a bus or car. Hold the acceleration detector in a vertical position and monitor the metal nut as the vehicle travels around town. Document and describe the metal nut's movement as you stop suddenly, turn, or speed up. Does the metal nut ever hit or touch the side of the bottle when the auto stops or speeds up suddenly?

 Journal Question People say they can "feel" acceleration. What are they actually feeling? Explain this feeling in terms of your new understanding from this lab.

TomanoNaoki/Wikimedia Commons

Try This!

Sit on a skateboard or wheeled cart on a smooth surface, such as a gym floor. Make sure your hands and feet aren't touching the floor. Ask a friend to throw a soccer ball to you. What happens when you catch the ball? Throw the ball forward as hard as you can. What happens?

Try the activity again, this time catching and throwing a balloon instead of a ball. Was there any difference? How can conservation of momentum help you explain what happened when you caught the ball? When you threw the ball? What would explain the difference in the results when you used the ball versus when you used the balloon?

In This Stage:

Your expedition goal is accomplished when you:

Can describe momentum.

Can explain how the conservation of momentum determines which accidents are deadly and which ones are not.

Why this is important:

Momentum is involved in the study of colliding objects. It forms the basis of understanding how and why car crashes can be deadly.

Words to Identify

momentum, inertia, law of conservation of momentum

Stage 3: When Paths Collide

Momentum

The cars and objects you have studied thus far in this expedition have sped up, slowed down, and turned. But what would happen if they were to crash into each other? What happens during car crashes is at the heart of what Matt Brumbelow explores at IIHS. And, while speed, velocity, and acceleration are critical to this understanding, another part of the explanation lies with momentum.

Momentum is an object's mass multiplied by its velocity. If the velocities of two objects are the same, the object with more mass will have more momentum. If the masses of two objects are the same, the object with a higher velocity will have more momentum.

Mass and Inertia

If something is perfectly still, does it have momentum? According to the formula for momentum, an object with zero velocity has zero momentum. However, it would be much more difficult to start rolling a boulder that was not moving than to start rolling a basketball that was not moving, even though neither has initial momentum.

The difference in effort needed to start rolling a motionless boulder compared to a motionless basketball can be explained by inertia. **Inertia** is an object's resistance to change in its state of motion. It describes the tendency of a motionless object to remain motionless and of a moving object to continue moving with the same velocity unless acted upon by an outside force. Like momentum, inertia is related to mass. The more mass an object has, the greater its inertia.

Like momentum, inertia makes it harder to stop or change the direction of a moving object. Since a moving object with a large mass has greater momentum and inertia than an object moving at the same velocity but with less mass, the more massive object is harder to stop. For example, if you tried to use your own strength to stop a car that is rolling down a hill, its mass would be hard to stop, even at low speeds. It would be much less difficult to stop a toy car rolling down the same hill at the same speed, since the toy car has much less mass than a real one.

Calculating Momentum

A truck with a mass of 1,200 kilograms traveled south at 7 meters per second. What was its momentum?

momentum = 1,200 kg × 7 m/s south

The truck had a momentum of 8,400 kg·m/s south.

A skier with a mass of 70 kg skied east downhill at 12 meters per second. What was his momentum?

momentum = 70 kg × 12 m/s east

The skier had a momentum of 840 kg·m/s east.

The relationship between an object's mass and its velocity (kg·m/s).

momentum = mass × velocity

The amount of matter in an object (kg).

The speed and direction of an object (meters/second).

Momentum and Collisions

Momentum is an important factor in determining what happens during collisions, including car crashes. One reason for this is that the more momentum an object has, the harder it is to stop. You could easily stop a basketball moving at 10 kilometers per hour, but you would have a much harder time stopping a huge boulder moving at the same speed. The boulder has more momentum than the basketball because it has more mass.

Conversely, think about skating or riding a skateboard. It would take very little effort to stop if you were moving along slowly. But if you were skating very fast down a ramp, it would be much more difficult to stop. This is because when you have more velocity, you have more momentum.

Remember that velocity is a vector quantity with both magnitude and direction. Since velocity is a factor in momentum, momentum is a vector quantity, too. Momentum plays an important role in car crashes. When two cars moving in the same direction crash into each other, the results can be very different than when two cars moving in opposite directions crash into each other.

For example, imagine a very small car going 65 kilometers per hour north, and a large truck moving 65 kilometers per hour south on a highway. Both vehicles are traveling the same speed. However, because they are traveling in different directions, they have different velocities. The large truck also has more mass than the small car.

What would happen if the two vehicles were to collide? Would the outcome be different if the car collided with another small car? Or if the truck collided with a car traveling in the same direction? Momentum is an important factor that determines the outcome of collisions.

▼ Momentum increases when either the mass or the velocity of an object increases.

Object	Mass	Velocity	Momentum
	0.05 kg	47 m/s	2.35 kg·m/s
	900 kg	10 m/s	9,000 kg·m/s
	75 kg	0 m/s	0 kg·m/s

Conservation of Momentum

What happens to momentum in a collision? The **law of conservation of momentum** tells us that momentum is neither lost nor gained, but rather is transferred between objects. For example, if a car begins to roll down a steep hill, it will gain velocity. If it were to crash into a parked car, some of its momentum would be transferred to the parked car, causing the parked car to move and the runaway car to slow down. The crash would likely cause some damage to the parked car as well.

What would happen if a train moving at the same velocity as the runaway car crashed into a parked car? The train's mass is far greater than the runaway car's mass, which means the train would have a significantly greater amount of momentum. The transfer of momentum to the parked car would cause the parked car to move even further, and the crash would probably result in a lot more damage.

The law of conservation of momentum can be used to predict how objects will react in a collision. Police use it, along with other factors, to reconstruct how car crashes happen.

In some cases, when two vehicles collide, they move independently from each other after impact. In other cases, the two vehicles collide and "stick together." When this occurs, the two objects move as one after the collision, and their momentum is combined.

Crash Test Dummies

One of the most important parts of Matt Brumbelow's job is measuring the acceleration of dummies inside test cars at IIHS. As part of his effort to reduce injuries to humans who are involved in car crashes, Matt analyzes the data collected during car crashes. Sensors inside the dummies collect data before, during, and after a crash. The data are then sent to computers. Matt uses the computers to analyze these data and calculate the different forces felt at different points on the dummies. Based upon the data and his knowledge of physics, Matt then suggests changes which need to be made in the manufacturing of the cars to reduce harmful forces on the human body.

Peter Haydock/The JASON Project

Check for Understanding

✓ What is the law of conservation of momentum, and how does it apply to car crashes?

▶ What happens to the momentum of a bowling ball when it hits pins? The bowling ball will slow down, but does that mean momentum is lost?

Fir0002/Wikimedia Commons

Visualizing Conservation of Momentum

The law of conservation of momentum states that momentum is neither lost or gained, but is transferred between objects. Below are examples of how that can happen.

BEFORE

A large truck is stopped in the road and a small car hits it from behind. The car has forward momentum, and the truck is not moving.

AFTER

Some of the car's momentum will be transferred to the truck, and the truck will move in the direction the car was traveling. The lighter car will rebound off the truck and move in the opposite direction.

BEFORE

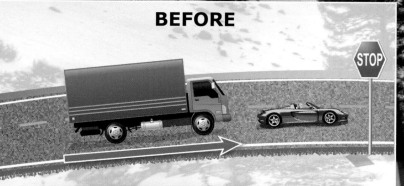

A small car is stopped at a stop sign and is hit from behind by a large truck. The two vehicles don't stick together.

AFTER

Both vehicles will move in the direction the truck was traveling. Since some of the truck's momentum is transferred to the car, the car will move faster, and the truck will slow down.

footloosiety/flickr

BEFORE

A small car is stopped at a stop sign and is hit by a large truck. The two vehicles stick together after the collision.

AFTER

Both vehicles will move as one with a combined momentum in the direction the truck was traveling.

BEFORE

Two cars of equal mass moving at the same speed collide head to head.

AFTER

Both cars will rebound and move at the same speed in opposite directions.

Steps Toward Road and Highway Safety

Tests conducted at IIHS show how speed, velocity, acceleration, and deceleration during car crashes can change the motion of the objects involved. Matt Brumbelow uses computer analyses of crash data to observe the changes in the motion of the cars and the crash test dummies. These data are used to determine how safety equipment, such as airbags and seatbelts, can help reduce impacts and ultimately, can reduce injuries. Collision data collected from the crash test dummies are used to improve and refine safety devices so the dummies get "injured" rather than you.

Testing at IIHS has lead to the introduction of many injury-preventive measures. These include mandatory seatbelt laws, information leading to specially designed airbags for head-on and side-on collisions, testing and improvements of booster seats used for small children, bumper designs that help reduce the impacts of a collision, and underride guard strength testing for large trucks. These measures are making our roads safer and are saving countless lives each year.

Ensuring the safety of drivers and passengers is the primary goal of Matt Brumbelow and the team of scientists and engineers at IIHS. Their hard work, determination, scientific observations, and analyses make it possible for automobile companies to improve the safety of vehicles year after year.

Fast Fact

Statistics show that wearing a seatbelt increases your chance of surviving a car crash by as much as 70 percent. Why are seatbelts such excellent protection in a crash? When you are riding in a car, you are in motion, and your velocity is the same as that of the car. In the case of a crash, the motion of your body would continue due to inertia. If the force that stops your motion is the windshield or the ground outside the car, you could be seriously injured. Seatbelts are designed to stop your motion more safely, resulting in less injury.

M.Minderhound/Wikimedia Commons

Check for Understanding

✓ Why is conservation of momentum important to the car crash tests done at IIHS?

JohnRobertShepherd/flickr

Momentum

As Matt Brumbelow and his team at IIHS explore car safety in a variety of crash scenarios, momentum plays a big role in their calculations. They must consider how momentum is transferred from one vehicle to another in order to accurately predict what will happen when vehicles of different masses and velocities collide.

In this activity, you will explore how momentum plays a role in vehicle collisions. You will apply critical thinking skills and hands-on inquiry as you explore the parameters of momentum as revealed through toy car crashes.

Materials
- Lab 3 Data Sheet
- two toy cars of different masses
- stopwatch
- duct tape
- marker
- several rulers or meter sticks
- balance/scale
- 1 piece of flat cardboard such as a flattened cardboard box
- assortment of books
- clay

Lab Prep

1. Obtain two toy cars of different masses. Use a balance to measure and record the mass of each car. Use tape and a marker to label the lighter car as "Car 1", and the heavier car as "Car 2."

2. Using books and a piece of flat cardboard, construct a ramp with a medium slope.

3. Create a lane for the toy cars to roll down by taping rulers or meter sticks onto the ramp. Continue the lane onto the flat area at the bottom of the ramp by taping down additional meter sticks or rulers.

Make Observations

1. Place a barrier such as a book at the bottom of the ramp. Measure and record the length of the ramp from the starting point to the barrier.

2. Place Car 1 at the top of the ramp and release it. Use a stopwatch to time how long it takes to reach the barrier at the bottom of the ramp. Repeat this three times, and average the results.

3. Calculate and record the average velocity of Car 1, using the formula: velocity = displacement / time. Calculate and record the average momentum of Car 1 using the formula: momentum = mass × velocity.

4. Place Car 2 at the base of the ramp. Place Car 1 at the top of the ramp. Make a prediction about what will happen when the vehicles collide.

5. Release Car 1. Start the stopwatch when Car 1 hits Car 2. Measure and record the time it takes Car 2 to stop moving. Measure and record how far from the impact site Car 2 traveled. Repeat this step three times.

6. Calculate and record the average time and average distance Car 2 moved. Calculate and record Car 2's velocity and momentum.

7. Add enough clay to the top of Car 1 to double its mass. Measure and record the new mass. Repeat steps 2-6, using the more massive Car 1.

8. Graph your data. Put "Mass of Car 1" on the x-axis and "Distance Car 2 Moved" on the y-axis.

9. Repeat step 7 by doubling the mass of Car 1 again.

Reflect and Apply

1. Explain how the momentum of Car 1 changed as the mass was increased.

Extension

Repeat the experiment, but remove the lanes at the base of the ramp, and vary the position of Car 2. How does the change in Car 2's position affect its movement after the collision?

Journal Question What are some potential design considerations engineers should bear in mind when developing new cars?

Performing Crash Tests

Recall that your expedition goal is to *investigate and analyze the factors that describe motion and position.* Now that you are fully briefed, it is time to analyze and understand how the variables of speed, velocity, acceleration, and momentum may affect the outcome of car crashes in hopes to develop safer vehicles for the road.

Matt Brumbelow and the team of researchers at the Insurance Institute for Highway Safety (IIHS) are interested in keeping people safe. By crashing cars together, they can analyze how the cars perform in different situations. Engineers and researchers can then use this information to develop safer designs, features, and materials for car manufacturers to

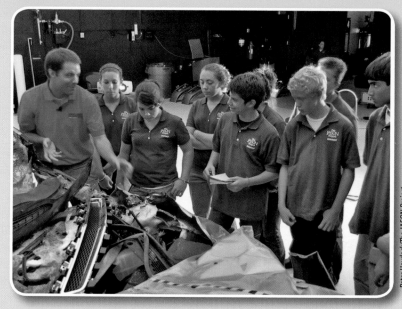

Peter Haydock/The JASON Project

use. As part of his analysis, Matt and the team collect a variety of information about each crash. Some of these data include videos of the crash from multiple angles and detailed information on the velocities of the cars. Using these data, the team can calculate the acceleration and momentum of the vehicles at different points of the test. All of these data can then be used to analyze how the cars perform, providing engineers insight into how they can make the cars even safer for passengers.

To begin this Field Assignment, you will analyze video and velocity data from two car crashes conducted by Matt at IIHS. Using this information, you will calculate the acceleration and momentum of the cars involved in these two crashes. Through your analysis, you will determine how each of these variables affected the outcome of the crashes. Using this knowledge, you will then create a device which will protect a raw egg from a crash to the ground. Like Matt and his team, you will collect video data and determine the velocity, acceleration, and momentum of your egg's crash protection device. From the data, you will then make recommendations for ways to improve the design to make the device safer for the egg.

Materials
- **Expedition 2 Field Assignment Data Sheet**
- **egg (raw)**
- **tape measure or meter stick**
- **tape**
- **materials provided by your instructor**
- **video camera**
- **camera tripod (optional)**
- **computer with video editing software and internet access**

Objectives:
- Graph and analyze velocity versus time data from a car crash conducted by Matt Brumbelow and his team.
- Calculate the acceleration of the vehicles at different points of the crash.
- View and analyze video footage of different car crashes.
- Construct a crash protection device for an egg.
- Test and analyze the speed, velocity, acceleration, and momentum of your crash protection device.
- Capture video footage of your device crashing to assist your analysis.
- Determine variables that affect the speed, velocity, acceleration, momentum, and fate of the egg.
- Develop strategies to improve the design of your crash protection device to make it safer for the egg.

Field Prep

1. Watch the two crash test videos from Matt Brumbelow and his team. Describe any similarities or differences in the way the cars react in the videos during the crash. What could be causing these differences?

2. Create two line graphs from the velocity vs. time data for the two car crashes in the videos. Label the x-axis "time" and the y-axis "velocity."

3. Use the graphs to describe what each car is doing during the following time intervals:
   a. Car 1
      i. 0–3 seconds
      ii. 3–8 seconds
      iii. 8–19 seconds
      iv. 19–19.5 seconds
   b. Car 2
      i. 0–4 seconds
      ii. 4–8 seconds
      iii. 10–16 seconds
      iv. 16–16.5 seconds

4. Calculate the acceleration for each car during the intervals in step 3. (Reminder: acceleration = change in velocity / change in time)

5. Using the graph, determine the time of impact for each car.

6. Calculate the momentum of each car at the moment of impact assuming both cars have a mass of 1,500 kg. (Reminder: momentum = mass × velocity)

7. Compare and contrast the results of the crash from the video with the acceleration and momentum you just calculated. What effect could these variables have on the outcome of the crash?

Expedition Challenge

1. Using the materials provided by your instructor, design a crash protection device for a raw egg.

2. Determine the mass of the completed device, including the egg.

3. Film your device falling from a standardized height as determined by your instructor.

4. From the video, determine how long it took for the device to reach each meter mark. Document this on your data sheet.

Expedition Debrief

1. Graph the distance vs. time data of your falling device. Plot time on the x-axis and distance on the y-axis in one-meter increments. Describe the shape of the graph.

2. Using the graph and your data, determine the velocity of the device at each meter mark.

3. Graph the velocity vs. time data for your falling device. Plot time on the x-axis and velocity on the y-axis. Describe the shape of the graph and how it relates to the device's changing velocity.

4. Use your data to calculate the momentum of the device right as it is about to strike the floor. (Reminder: momentum = mass × velocity)

5. Divide the total time of the falling device into five equal segments.

6. Use these time intervals to make marks along the x-axis of your velocity vs. time graph.

7. Calculate the acceleration within each of these time intervals using your velocity vs. time graph. (Reminder: acceleration = change in velocity / change in time)

8. Based on all of the data, develop strategies to improve the design of your crash protection device.

Journal Question Develop a proposal to your community leaders with recommendations for locations to focus road and collision studies that could reduce the number of crashes in these locations.

Peter Haydock/The JASON Project

Expedition 2: Motion

Continue to explore the concepts and formulas that describe motion by solving the problems on these pages.

Calculating Speed

Speed is the distance travelled over a specific period of time.

Sample Problem

Kimberly completes a 450 meter obstacle course on her dirt bike in 60 seconds. What is her speed for the course?

Understanding the Problem:

What information does the problem give you?

Distance: 450 m
Time: 60 seconds

What are you trying to find out?
speed

What formula do you need?
speed = distance / time

speed = distance / time

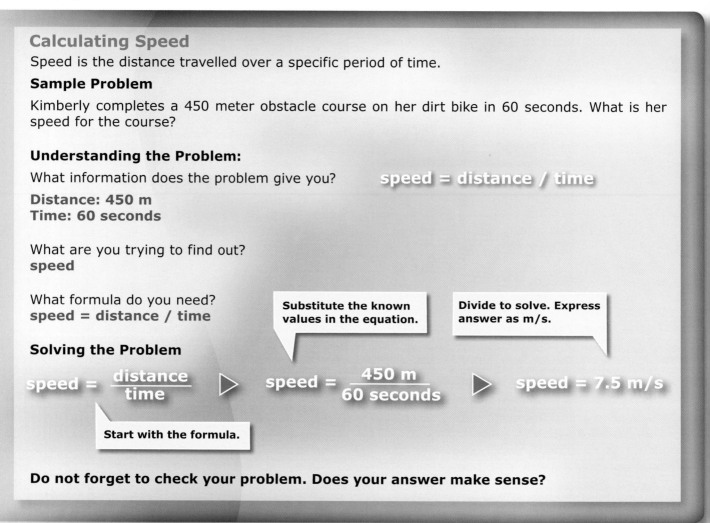

Solving the Problem

$$\text{speed} = \frac{\text{distance}}{\text{time}} \quad \triangleright \quad \text{speed} = \frac{450 \text{ m}}{60 \text{ seconds}} \quad \triangleright \quad \text{speed} = 7.5 \text{ m/s}$$

Start with the formula.

Substitute the known values in the equation.

Divide to solve. Express answer as m/s.

Do not forget to check your problem. Does your answer make sense?

Try These

- Henry drives about 1,120 km from Baltimore, MD, to Atlanta, GA. It takes him 14 hours to get there. What is Henry's speed for the trip?

- Sarah takes a two hour flight from Cincinnati, OH, to Austin, TX. The plane travels 1,565 km during the trip. How fast was the plane flying?

- Noah finishes a 50 m race in 10 seconds. Lee finishes a 30 m race in 50 seconds. Who is the faster runner and how do you know?

- Mark leaves his house and jogs at an average speed of 3 km per hour for 45 minutes to reach his friend's house. How far does he live from his friend?

- Jake's sister calls at noon and asks him to pick her up at the airport at 4:00. The airport is 480 km away. If Jake leaves immediately and drives an average of 96 km/h to stay within the speed limit, will he arrive in time, early, or late to meet his sister? Explain how you know.

Fast Fact

The symbol Δ is used in mathematical formulas to represent change. For example Δt represents a change in time. To calculate a change in time you subtract the starting time from the ending time. The same can be done to calculate changes in distance (Δd), velocity (Δv), and many other units.

Calculating Velocity

Velocity is the speed of an object in a given direction.

Sample Problem

Vancouver is approximately 225 kilometers north of Seattle. What is the average velocity of a bus traveling directly from Seattle to Vancouver if the trip takes 3 hours?

Understanding the Problem:

What information does the problem give you?

Distance: 225 km
Time: 3 hours

velocity = displacement / time

What are you trying to find out?
velocity of the bus

What formula do you need?

$$v = \frac{d}{t}$$

Solving the Problem

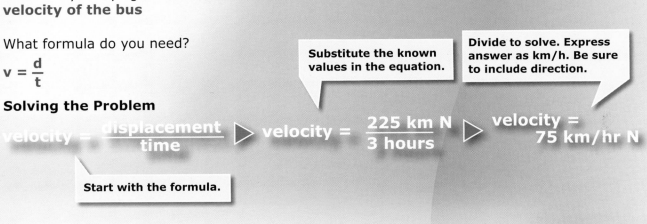

velocity = $\frac{\text{displacement}}{\text{time}}$ ▷ velocity = $\frac{\text{225 km N}}{\text{3 hours}}$ ▷ velocity = 75 km/hr N

Start with the formula.

Substitute the known values in the equation.

Divide to solve. Express answer as km/h. Be sure to include direction.

Do not forget to check your problem. Does your answer make sense?

Try These

- Jake jogs 2 km east along the river. He jogs for half an hour. What is his average velocity?

- Paul lives 9 miles south of his friend Sam. It takes Paul 45 minutes to bike to Paul's house. What is Paul's velocity for the trip?

- Jerry and Amy both arrive at school at 8:30 a.m. Jerry left his house at 8:00 a.m. and travelled 3 km north to the school. Amy left her house at 7:00 a.m. and traveled 12 km east to the school. Compare Jerry's and Amy's velocities and write a statement explaining who travelled with the greatest average velocity.

- If Jerry travels to Amy's house with a velocity of 7 km/h NW, how long will it take him to get there? Use the information given in the previous problem to draw a picture of Jerry's and Amy's houses and the school, and then use the Pythagorean theorem to solve.

- Ariel's school is on one side of a large park, and her house is on the other side. To get to school, Ariel can drive 3 km E, 1 km S, and 3 km W around the park to the school at an average of 35 km/h, or she can jog directly south to school through the park at 5 km/h. Draw a picture to determine Ariel's displacement from the school when she is at home. Explain whether jogging or driving will get her to school faster and why.

Calculating Acceleration

Acceleration is the rate at which velocity changes. Acceleration can describe increasing speed, decreasing speed, or a change in direction.

Sample Problem

A car leaves a stop sign traveling south and accelerates from 0 m/s to 30 m/s in 10 seconds. What is its rate of acceleration?

Understanding the Problem:

What information does the problem give you?

Change in acceleration: 0 m/s to 30 m/s
Time: 10 seconds

What are you trying to find out?
the car's acceleration

acceleration = change in velocity / time ($a = \Delta v / \Delta t$)

What formula do you need?
$a = \Delta v / \Delta t$

Solving the Problem

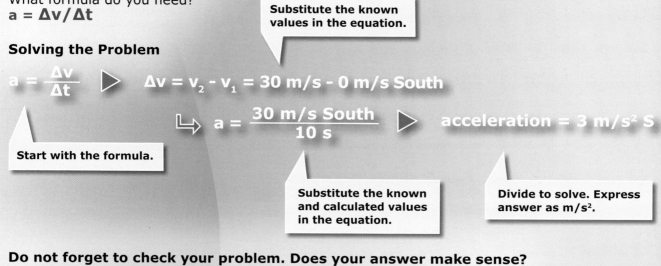

Substitute the known values in the equation.

$$a = \frac{\Delta v}{\Delta t}$$

$$\Delta v = v_2 - v_1 = 30 \text{ m/s} - 0 \text{ m/s South}$$

Start with the formula.

$$a = \frac{30 \text{ m/s South}}{10 \text{ s}}$$

$$\text{acceleration} = 3 \text{ m/s}^2 \text{ S}$$

Substitute the known and calculated values in the equation.

Divide to solve. Express answer as m/s².

Do not forget to check your problem. Does your answer make sense?

Try These

- When the start gun sounds at the track meet, Blake accelerates from 0 m/s to 5 m/s in 15 seconds. If Blake runs east, what is his acceleration from the start line?

- A car enters the interstate going north and accelerates from 35 km/hr to 95 km/hr in 30 seconds. What is the car's acceleration?

- A car traveling south slows down from 30 m/s to 5 m/s in 10 seconds. What is the car's acceleration?

- Henry runs at 3 m/s E and then accelerates at a rate of 1.5 m/s² E for 3 seconds. What is his final velocity?

- Sam races her friend to the ball, running at 7 m/s N. She realizes that she dropped her water bottle and runs S for 10 seconds at 8 m/s to get it. What is her acceleration?

Calculating Momentum (p)

Momentum is a characteristic of moving objects. It describes the relationship between an object's mass and its velocity.

Sample Problem

An 1,000 kg car is traveling west at 18 m/s. What is its momentum?

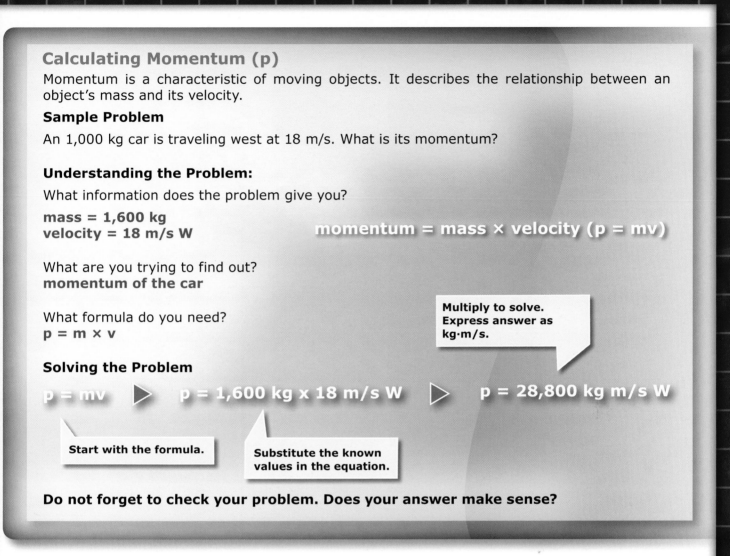

Understanding the Problem:

What information does the problem give you?

mass = 1,600 kg
velocity = 18 m/s W

momentum = mass × velocity (p = mv)

What are you trying to find out?
momentum of the car

What formula do you need?
p = m × v

Multiply to solve. Express answer as kg·m/s.

Solving the Problem

p = mv ▷ **p = 1,600 kg x 18 m/s W** ▷ **p = 28,800 kg m/s W**

Start with the formula.

Substitute the known values in the equation.

Do not forget to check your problem. Does your answer make sense?

Try These

- Jenny's bike has a mass of 12 kilograms. If she is riding east down a hill at 5 m/s, what is her momentum?
- A 3,000 kg truck is traveling south at 15 m/s. What is its momentum?
- A 2,000 kg sedan is traveling west at 25 m/s. How would the sedan's momentum change if it slowed down to 10 m/s?
- Sid has a momentum of 550 kg·m/s skating north downhill. If Sid and his skateboard together have a mass of 50 kg, what is Sid's velocity?
- Whitney runs out of gas in her 1,500 kg car at the top of the hill. There is a gas station halfway up the next hill, but Whitney will need to have a momentum of 26,850 kg·m/s to reach the gas station. How fast will she need to be traveling at the bottom of the hill in order to reach the gas station?

cupcakes2/flickr

Home Run

Whether you have realized it or not, you have often seen physics at play. Sports such as baseball, football, cycling, hockey, and soccer, rely on physics. Physics governs how balls spin and move, players' actions and reactions, and even which shoes are best for the sport.

In baseball, drag and the related aerodynamic force, lift, are key. In fact, if it were not for these forces, pitchers like Nolan Ryan, could not throw a curveball. Drag acts in the opposite direction of the motion of the baseball and helps to slow its velocity. Lift acts vertically on the ball. When a pitcher releases a curveball, he spins it in such as way that the seams disrupt the lift, creating a high-pressure zone on the top of the ball. Working with the force of gravity, this causes the curveball to drop more quickly as it hurls toward the batter at speeds up to 90 miles per hour. Spinning the ball the other way can have the opposite effect—the ball actually moves upward.

Assuming the batter can connect with the ball—a tricky thing to do with a curveball—conservation of momentum comes into play. Why does the batter swing instead of just holding the bat out for the ball to hit?

deusxflorida/flickr

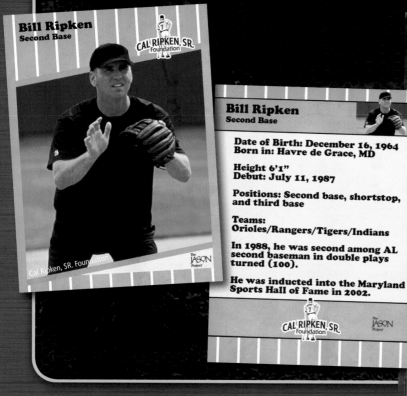

Bill Ripken
Second Base

CAL RIPKEN, SR.
Foundation

Cal Ripken, SR. Foundation

The JASON Project

Bill Ripken
Second Base

Date of Birth: December 16, 1964
Born in: Havre de Grace, MD

Height 6'1"
Debut: July 11, 1987

Positions: Second base, shortstop, and third base

Teams:
Orioles/Rangers/Tigers/Indians

In 1988, he was second among AL second baseman in double plays turned (100).

He was inducted into the Maryland Sports Hall of Fame in 2002.

CAL RIPKEN, SR.
Foundation

The JASON Project

LET'S MOVE!

To protect your heart and protect your health, you need to experience Newton's Laws for yourself. The best way to feel Newton's Laws is to go out and get moving! All children need at least an hour of physical activity every day—and adults need at least 30 minutes. Make a family goal to "study" Newton's Laws in action. Ride a bike, shoot some hoops, or jump rope. Do whatever it takes to get moving and get healthy in the process.

For more information and ideas for ways to get moving, visit **www.letsmove.gov**.

kgsandsoccer/flickr

Cal Ripken, Jr.
Shortstop

Date of Birth: August 24, 1960
Born in: Havre de Grace, MD
Height: 6'4"
Nickname: Iron Man
Debut: August 10, 1981
Team: Orioles
Positions: shortstop, third base
Records Set:
 Home runs (431)
 Hits (3,184)
 Consecutive Games Played (2,632)
Hall of Fame: inducted in 2007

Cal Ripken, SR. Foundation

The JASON Project

CAL RIPKEN, SR.
Foundation

The JASON Project

SEC 2   ROW 15   SEAT 9

World Championship

CAL'S

PREMIER

BASEBALL

GAME

Many of you may dream about being the next great star—and shooting the winning goal—or hitting that home run in front of millions. So go out there and do it. With practice, hard work, determination, and confidence, you too can see your name on the back of a trading card. But what do you do if you don't have safe places to play and be active? This foundation is there to help. The Cal Ripken, Sr. Foundation partners with communities across the country to provide facilities where kids can safely play and learn. Does your school or community need a new park? Develop a plan, and then visit: **www.ripkenfoundation.org** to share your ideas.

He swings to increase the momentum the bat has when it collides with the ball. That momentum is then transferred to the ball. Added to the momentum the ball already has as it speeds toward the batter, this momentum can carry the ball over the fence.

The more momentum the ball has, the further it can travel through the air before the forces of drag and gravity cause it to decelerate toward the ground. That is why home run hitters like Cal Ripkin, Jr. have to hit the ball with so much force—they want to overcome drag and gravity for as long as they can.

Drag, lift, and momentum are important factors in football and soccer as well. For example, when the ball is kicked, it gains momentum from the player's foot. Field goal kickers must consider the drag and the force of gravity on the football in order to arc it at the right angle to go through the field goal. Soccer players can take advantage of lift to make the goalie's job really difficult. By putting spin on the ball, they can cause it to curve unexpectedly as it shoots past the goalie.

yuki/flickr

Your Turn

What is your favorite sport? Examine your favorite sport with physics in mind. Identify and research some ways that physics governs the game. Create a tip sheet for players of your sport with suggestions on ways to use physics to improve their game.

dave hogg/flickr

deusxflorida/flickr

"It is a huge adventure to take the basics of physics, like Newton's Laws of Motion, and use these fundamentals to successfully launch, land, and deploy research tools, like the rover, in order to learn something new about the universe."

—Kobie Boykins
Mechanical Engineer, NASA's Jet Propulsion Laboratory

Kobie Boykins

At NASA's Jet Propulsion Laboratory (JPL), Kobie Boykins uses his knowledge of physics to help design and build robotic rovers, such as Curiosity, which study the surfaces of other planets like Mars to determine if these planets could sustain life.

Meet the Researcher Video
Join Kobie behind the scenes at NASA's Jet Propulsion Laboratory to see how he uses his knowledge of forces and motion to help unlock the mysteries of Mars.

Mechanical Engineer, NASA's Jet Propulsion Laboratory

Read more about Kobie online in the JASON Expedition Center.

Peter Haydock/The JASON Project

Photo Credits (left to right): AsturKon/Wikimedia; Lisa Thayne/The JASON Project; NASA; MarcusObal/Wikimedia; NASA JPL; Peter Haydock/The JASON Project

Your Expedition Goal...

Apply your knowledge of forces and Newton's Laws of Motion to explore the universe around you.

To accomplish your expedition goal successfully, you will need to

- Define force and explain how forces act on matter.
- Identify the many forces acting on an object to determine the net force on the object.
- Explore the relationship between force, mass, and acceleration.
- Apply Newton's Laws of Motion to understand how forces affect an object's motion.
- Evaluate the impact of forces and motion on society, technological advances, and the exploration of our universe.
- Investigate the relationships among weight, volume, density, and pressure.

Join the Team

Join the Argonauts as they study forces with Kobie Boykins, an engineer from NASA's Jet Propulsion Laboratory (JPL) in Pasadena, California. Kobie was an engineer for the Mars rovers *Spirit* and *Opportunity*. He is currently working on the next generation Mars rover, *Curiosity*. This new rover is much larger than *Spirit* and *Opportunity*, which required engineers to design new landing mechanisms. Kobie and Argonauts (L to R): Marty Kelsey, Aubrey Gonzalez, Maggie Botros, and Kieana Yasunaka work with a vibration table at JPL to test parts before they are launched into space.

May the Force be With You

Excitement sweeps through the Jet Propulsion Laboratory (JPL) mission control room as the Mars Science Laboratory slowly lowers the robotic rover, *Curiosity*, toward the ground. Back in mission control, Kobie Boykins and other NASA engineers sit at their stations as the countdown begins. Even though they have been in this situation before, this is a critical moment—as many years of work leading up to this point are being tested in preparation for their next Mars mission.

Will the new tether landing system work? Have all the forces been calculated correctly? With all of the updates made since the previous Mars rovers, *Spirit* and *Opportunity*, what unknown obstacle might cause it to crash into the surface? Centimeter by centimeter, *Curiosity* slowly approaches the surface. Every square centimeter of the craft reacts to the variety of forces acting upon it. Then, as *Curiosity* safely touches down, the crowd erupts into cheers and high fives, while Kobie breathes a sigh of relief.

But, their work isn't over yet. This was only one of many test runs completed at the JPL facility before the actual launch to Mars. Similar to the successful tests conducted before launching the rovers *Spirit* and *Opportunity* in 2003, these tests are an essential part of launching new, unmanned spacecraft to other planets. And, after *Curiosity* finishes roaming the surface of Mars to determine if it is capable of supporting life, Kobie and the other scientists at NASA will begin developing the next, cutting-edge, robotic device to continue exploring Mars and beyond.

Similar to these rovers, you encounter a full range of forces, motion, and energy every day. In fact, the interactions of forces that make a landing on Mars possible are the same forces that impact people and objects on Earth. As you explore forces further, you will better understand how they impact not only Mars rovers, but also your everyday life.

NASA JPL

Expedition 3 Briefing Video Prepare for your expedition by viewing this briefing on your objectives. Learn how scientists, such as Kobie Boykins, use clues to better understand how forces impact objects on Earth, and in space.

In This Stage:

Your expedition goal is accomplished when you:

Know how forces influence an object's motion.

Understand Newton's Laws, and how they describe the relationship between force and mass.

Why this is important:

Understanding forces allows us to predict the movement of objects, so we can better navigate our environment.

Words to Identify

force, newton, net force, friction, free-body diagram, inertia, unbalanced force, balanced force, thrust, coefficient of friction, static friction, kinetic friction, sliding friction, rolling friction, fluid friction

Expedition Briefing

Stage 1: The Nature of Forces and Inertia

Force

Look out the window on a windy day and you might see the leaves on a tree moving. In the classroom, you might see a pencil roll across your desk and stop, or a book fall from a desk to the floor. All around you, objects move, change direction, come to a stop, or remain still. All of states of motion—or lack of motion—are caused by forces.

A **force** is anything, such as a push or pull, that causes a change in the motion of a freely moveable object, or that causes stress in a non-moving object. Force is a vector quantity, so it is described by both its magnitude, or strength, and the direction in which it acts. Force is measured in the SI unit **newtons**. You might exert a strong force to push your chair away from you, or a smaller force to pull a pencil toward you.

As you investigate forces further, you will begin to understand how and why objects move, change directions, stop, or even remain motionless. From atoms to galaxies, every object in the universe is affected by forces. We can use our understanding of forces to develop technologies that control and utilize forces more efficiently as we develop solutions to things like cleaner energy production on Earth, safer car crashes, and explore our mysterious universe.

A Universe of Forces

Have you ever wondered how it is possible to launch a spacecraft here on Earth and actually land it on Mars, more than 56 million kilometers away? Forces are at the heart of this answer. Kobie Boykins of NASA's Jet Propulsion Laboratory (JPL) in Pasadena, California, applies his understanding of forces to help plan such missions to study Mars.

Kobie Boykins' current mission is to send the unmanned rover, *Curiosity*, to Mars. The rover will land on the Martian surface and relay information back to scientists on Earth. Will *Curiosity* find evidence of life or water? Will this information bring us closer to living on Mars? It all depends on what the rover finds.

Net Force

Launching a robot from Earth to the surface of Mars is not an easy task. To accomplish this job, Kobie Boykins must anticipate the **net force** acting on *Curiosity* at all times. Net force is the sum of all forces acting on an object at any given moment.

Forces with different strengths, or magnitudes, will act upon *Curiosity* in different directions throughout its mission. These combinations of forces can cause *Curiosity* to change direction, accelerate, stop, or even remain motionless.

As *Curiosity* is outfitted for its mission, it sits motionless on a platform at JPL, even though forces are acting on it. The gravity of the planet exerts a downward force on the rover and platform below it. At the same time, the platform exerts an equal upward force. Since these forces are equal but in opposite directions, they cancel each other out, and the net force acting on it is zero.

Example

One newton is equal to the force needed to accelerate a one-kilogram mass at a rate of one meter per second squared. The newton is named after Sir Isaac Newton, who was the first to explain the relationship between force, mass, and acceleration.

Now suppose a team of engineers at JPL wanted to have the rover move around the platform. To make this happen they would need to send a command to the rover to start the motors that turn the wheels. However, if the force the motor and wheels apply is not greater than friction, *Curiosity* will remain still. **Friction** is the force exerted on two touching surfaces, causing a resistance in motion. In the rover's case, the force between the surface of the platform and the surface of the wheels is just one source of friction. Additional sources of friction between the surfaces of the gears, bearings, and parts inside the motor and wheels add to the overall friction that the rover must overcome to move. Friction usually acts in the opposite direction of an applied force.

As long as the motor and wheels do not push *Curiosity* with a force greater than friction, the net force will remain zero, and the rover's position will not change. However, suppose the engineers send a command to the motor to provide more force to the wheels. As soon as the force applied by the motor and wheels becomes greater than the force due to friction between *Curiosity* and the platform, the net force would no longer be zero, and the rover would move in the direction of the applied force.

Check for Understanding

✓ Define force and give an example where forces apply.

| 60N | 60N | = 0 (balanced) | 80N | 20N | 60N | 50N + 40N | 70N | 20N |

Lisa Thayne/The JASON Project

Drawing-Free Body Diagrams

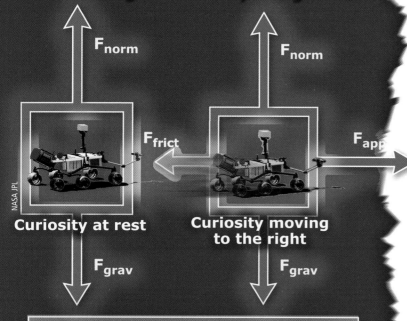

F$_{norm}$

F$_{norm}$

F$_{frict}$

F$_{app}$

NASA JPL

Curiosity at rest

Curiosity moving to the right

F$_{grav}$

F$_{grav}$

Recall that force is a vector and is visualized using arrows. The length of the arrow indicates the magnitude of the force, and the arrowhead points in the direction of the force.

1. Draw a box to represent an object resting on your desk.

2. Draw an arrow from the center of the box downward.

3. Label this arrow F$_{grav}$ (this arrow represents the force your object exerts on your desk due to gravity).

4. Draw an arrow the same size from the center of the box upward.

5. Label this arrow F$_{norm}$ (this arrow represents the normal force your desk exerts on the object you selected).

6. Move the object to the right, and draw an arrow from the center of the box to the right.

7. Label this arrow F$_{app}$ (this arrow represents the applied force you used to push your object to the right).

8. Draw a corresponding arrow from the center of the box to the left. If your object moves, this arrow should be shorter than the arrow from step 6.

9. Label this arrow F$_{frict}$ (this arrow is drawn in the opposite direction of the push because it represents the friction between the object and your desk).

Free-Body Diagrams

Many of the forces acting on *Curiosity*, such as gravity and friction, are not visible. **Free-body diagrams** are used to help visualize these forces. A free-body diagram acts as a map of all the forces acting on an object in a given situation. Vector arrows are used to show the magnitude, or strength, and direction of all forces in relation to each other.

When engineers are designing each part of *Curiosity's* mission, such as its landing on Mars, they must consider the magnitude and direction of every force acting on the rover. Free-body diagrams are a good way to account for all of these forces.

Balanced and Unbalanced Forces

In a game of tug-of-war, a flag is tied to the middle of a strong rope, and two teams pull on the rope in opposite directions. If one team can pull the rope so that the flag moves a certain distance in its direction, then that team wins. Because the winning team is exerting a greater force on the rope than the other team, the net force applied to the rope is not zero. These forces are described as unbalanced.

Now imagine a tug-of-war where both teams are pulling as hard as they can, but the flag remains motionless. The flag is motionless because both teams are exerting an equal amount of force on the rope, but in opposite directions. We know that forces are being exerted, but because the flag is motionless, the net force on the rope is zero. These forces are described as being balanced.

Check for Understanding

✓ What information is needed to draw a free-body diagram of an object?

NASA

Curiosity's Journey

Launch: When the rockets which blast *Curiosity* into space are ignited, the forces are unbalanced. The rockets' upward force is greater than the downward force of gravity on the shuttle.

Transit (Earth to Mars): When jets turn on in space to steer *Curiosity* toward Mars, the forces are again unbalanced. The Mars rover moves in the direction of the greater force created by the jets' **thrust**.

Landing: When the rover lands on Mars' surface, the forces become balanced once again.

F_{app}

F_{grav}

▲ Similar to rockets on the Atlas V rocket which carries *Curiosity* into space, the rockets on the space shuttle create an upward force that is greater than the downward force of gravity and the force of friction from Earth's atmosphere.

Example

In order to overcome the pull of gravity and leave Earth's atmosphere, the space shuttle must travel at over 27,000 kilometers per hour. The Law of Inertia presented a unique problem for early NASA engineers who needed to make sure astronauts could survive slowing down from these speeds. Because of their inertia, astronauts would tend to keep moving at these high speeds even after the space shuttle itself had slowed down or stopped. Engineers needed to design something that would exert enough force on astronauts traveling at high speeds to safely stop them. Using a series of tests on a sled track built just for that purpose, engineers designed a super seatbelt that would act on astronauts to overcome their inertia and keep them safely in their seats.

Motion and Inertia

A book will remain closed until someone opens it. A sheet of paper will sit on a desk until a gust of wind blows it off the desk. *Curiosity* will not blast off inside the Atlas V launch system until the rockets are ignited. These objects move because of forces. Without forces, they will continue to remain at rest indefinitely.

To you, this may seem like common sense. However, this universal law of nature was not identified until the late 1600s by Sir Isaac Newton. Newton, an English philosopher, mathematician, and physicist, is considered to be one of the world's most influential scientists. He described three universal laws of forces and motion, which can be applied to everything that moves here on Earth and in the universe.

Newton's First Law

When you are riding in a vehicle and the driver suddenly slams on the brakes to stop, you probably notice that you and other objects in the car quickly move forward. The reason why this happens has to do with inertia. **Inertia** is the tendency of an object to resist any change in its motion. This means that an object that is moving will continue to move with the same velocity, until an **unbalanced force** acts on it to stop it, change its speed, or change its direction. This also means that an object that is motionless will remain motionless unless an unbalanced force acts on it.

Newton's First Law

First Law: Unless a force changes its motion or direction, a motionless object will remain motionless, and an object in motion will continue moving at a constant velocity.

Even though the vehicle you are riding in is slowing down to a stop, your body resists this change in motion and tries to continue moving forward at the same velocity with which it was originally moving. You may also notice that when the stopped car starts speeding up, you move backward. Because of your inertia, you have a tendency to remain still while the car moves around you, making you feel like you are moving backwards. And even though cars did not exist when Isaac Newton was alive, the laws he wrote informed us about what would happen inside of them when we finally did create them.

The greater the mass of an object, the greater its inertia. Imagine trying to move a pebble compared to a massive boulder. Both objects are moveable; however, due to the difference in inertia, the force required to move them is considerably different. The boulder has more mass than the pebble, and therefore greater inertia. Because of this, it would require a lot more force to move or change the direction of movement of the boulder as compared to the pebble. Also, once that boulder starts moving, it would take a lot more force to stop it from moving.

PHILOSOPHIÆ
NATURALIS
PRINCIPIA
MATHEMATICA.

Autore J.S. NEWTON Trin. Coll. Cantab. Soc. Matheseos Professore Lucasiano, & Societatis Regalis Sodali.

IMPRIMATUR.
S. PEPYS, Reg. Soc. PRÆSES.
Julii 5. 1686.

LONDINI,
Jussu Societatis Regiæ ac Typis Josephi Streater. Prostat apud plures Bibliopolas. Anno MDCLXXXVII.

Public Domain/National Portrait Gallery, London

Andrew Dunn/Wikimedia Commons

Check for Understanding

✓ Describe Newton's First Law.

✓ How does Newton's First Law apply to a boulder sitting on top of a mountain?

Team Highlight

The Argonauts work with Kobie and JPL computer numeral control machinist Cliff Lengtat to manufacture a part for the upcoming space mission GRAIL, which will study the gravity of Earth. The Argos operated a Vertical Milling Machine to cut a piece of aluminum to an accuracy of one ten-thousandth of an inch.

Peter Haydock/
The JASON Project

Peter Haydock/The JASON Project

Try This!

Place a wooden block on top of a toy car. Predict what would happen to the car and the block if you pushed the car into a book. Try it and observe what happens. Explain what you see using Newton's First Law.

Friction and Motion

If objects in motion stay in motion, why do our cars need engines? Why do you have to continue to pedal to keep your bike moving? Obviously, we watch things slow down and stop every day, so how is this consistent with Newton's First Law? The answer lies in friction. Friction, the force that two touching surfaces exert on each other resists motion between them. Friction is present everywhere in the world, so it has a real impact on how we experience Newton's First Law.

The amount of friction present depends on how hard two surfaces push together, as well as, the characteristics of the surfaces in contact. The surface characteristics are described by the **coefficient of friction**—the degree of resistance of a surface. The greater the coefficient of friction is between any two objects, the more force is required to move the objects and keep them in motion. Rough surfaces such as grass have a higher coefficient of friction than smooth surfaces such as ice. Therefore, if you rolled a soccer ball across a grass field and an ice rink, it would travel further across the ice rink before coming to a stop.

Friction can be classified as either static or kinetic. **Static friction** acts on objects that are not moving. **Kinetic friction** acts on objects that are in motion. Kinetic friction can be further broken down into three basic types: sliding, rolling, and fluid. More force is usually needed to overcome static friction than kinetic friction.

Check for Understanding

✓ What is friction, and how does it affect motion?

✓ Describe static and kinetic friction.

✓ Describe why kinetic friction can be broken down into more basic types of friction.

Main Types of Friction

Static Friction

Static friction opposes the movement of a stationary object. When trying to slide a piece of furniture into place, the hardest part is often getting it moving.

Mike Wiltshire/Wikimedia Commons

Kinetic Friction

Kinetic friction acts on objects that are in motion. Once an object starts sliding, it generally requires less force to keep it in motion. There are three types of kinetic friction: **sliding**, **rolling**, and **fluid**.

Sliding

Occurs when two objects slide past one another. Basketball players take advantage of **sliding friction** when they wear shoes with rough rubber soles to prevent them from slipping when they stop or pivot.

Moritz/Wikimedia Commons

Rolling

Occurs when an object such as a wheel or a ball rolls across a surface. **Rolling friction** is usually easier to overcome than sliding friction. Skateboarders use small, hard wheels to reduce rolling friction on smooth surfaces like skateboard ramps.

Luis Cernadas Iglesias/Wikimedia Commons

Fluid

Occurs when a solid object moves through fluids like air. Cyclists use aerodynamic helmets and wear spandex to reduce **fluid friction** and increase their speed.

Brendan Gray/Wikimedia Commons

A Touch of Force

When the Mars rover *Curiosity* moves across the surface of Mars, many forces will be acting on it. In order to safely navigate the rover across the surface of the planet, Kobie Boykins and his team must understand how forces, including friction, gravity, and normal force, act on it. In this activity, you will have the opportunity to explore the balanced and unbalanced forces acting on a block of wood as it moves and explore how friction influences the amount of force needed to move the block.

Materials
- **Lab 1 Data Sheet**
- **3 wood blocks**
- **sandpaper**
- **duct tape**
- **spring scale**
- **string**
- **clay**

Lab Prep

1. Obtain 3 wood blocks. Put sandpaper on the bottom of one block with the grain facing outward. Put duct tape on the bottom of another with the sticky side against the wood.

2. Measure the mass of each block. Add clay to the top of the blocks as needed so that they all have an equal mass.

3. Use a spring scale to determine the weight of one wood block or measure the mass and convert to newtons.

4. Place one of the wood blocks on the table and determine the normal force applied upward by the table.

5. Draw a free-body diagram around the wood block sitting motionless on the table. Include the normal and gravitational forces next to their arrows.

6. Attach one end of a piece of string to the plain wood block and the other to a spring scale.

Make Observations

1. Pull the plain block with the spring scale and measure the amount of applied force needed to get the block moving, or overcome the frictional force of the table top. Pull the string very slowly and record the force as soon as it "levels out."

2. Draw a free-body diagram of the block when it overcomes friction and begins moving. Include as many force values as possible next to the arrows, such as the normal, gravitational, and applied force.

3. Repeat steps 1 and 2 using the sandpaper block.

4. Repeat steps 1 and 2 using the duct tape block.

Reflect and Apply

1. Based on your data, explain which surface (wood, sandpaper, duct tape) created the highest frictional force.

2. Identify and explain any time during the trials where some of the forces acting on the block were balanced or unbalanced.

Extension
Repeat the experiment with additional variables, such as surface area of the object touching the table, mass, or material creating friction, to determine their effect on the force required to move the object.

 Journal Question How does an understanding of balanced and unbalanced forces enable scientists like Kobie Boykins to drive unmanned rovers across the surface of other planets? How can they use this understanding to create strategies to reduce friction?

In This Stage:

Your expedition goal is accomplished when you:

Know how gravitational force and acceleration are related.

Know how Newton described the relationship between force, mass, and acceleration.

Why this is important:

Newton's Second and Third Laws allow us to calculate force and predict motion on Earth and in different parts of our solar system.

Words to Identify

gravity, acceleration, Newton's Second Law of Motion, Newton's Third Law of Motion, gravitational force (g-force), action-reaction force, gravitational acceleration (g), weight, mass

Stage 2: The Nature of Forces and Acceleration

Acceleration

Imagine yourself sitting on a bike at the top of a large hill. As you release the brakes, and the force of **gravity** takes over, you start speeding up, or accelerating. As your leg muscles apply force to the pedals, you accelerate even more to speeds faster than you have ever gone.

As you learned in Expedition 2, **acceleration** is the rate at which velocity changes over time. If a force—such as the force of your muscles on the pedals of your bicycle—increases in one direction, your velocity will increase and you will accelerate. If a force is applied in the opposite direction, your velocity will decrease and you will decelerate. For example, when you apply the brakes on your bike at the bottom of the hill, the brake pads squeeze the rim of the tire, creating friction. Friction acts in the opposite direction of the tires' motion, causing deceleration.

Newton's Second Law

As you explore your environment, you may start to notice the relationship between force and acceleration. **Newton's Second Law of Motion** explains the relationship between net force, mass, and the acceleration of objects. It states that, when a force is applied to an object, the object will accelerate. The relationship between force and acceleration is described in the equation: force equals an object's mass multiplied by its acceleration **(F = m × a)**.

Newton's First Law states that objects with greater mass or inertia require more force to move. The spacecraft carrying the Mars rover needs to accelerate to a certain velocity in order to escape Earth's atmosphere. If *Curiosity* has too much mass, the rockets may not have enough force to reach space, sending the mission crashing back down to Earth. However, Kobie Boykins can apply his knowledge of Newton's Second Law in order to overcome this inertia and launch *Curiosity* into space.

Check for Understanding

✓ Describe Newton's Second Law in terms of a rocket traveling in space.

Radfahrer_Winterberg/WikimediaCommons

Newton's Second Law

Anything, such as a push or pull, that causes a change in the motion of a freely moveable object, or that causes stress in a fixed object.

Force = mass × acceleration

Amount of matter in an object (kg).

Rate at which velocity changes over time (m/s²).

Motion and Gravitational Force

Picture yourself standing at the open door of a helicopter, hovering some 3,000 meters (9,843 feet) in the air. After checking your parachute for the last time, you jump out and accelerate head first toward Earth. During this type of free-fall when skydiving, the acceleration of a person is caused by the force of gravity between the mass of the person and the mass of Earth.

mrmac04/morgueFile

Terminal Velocity

There is a point at which an object moving in a fluid (such as air) cannot move any faster. When we think about the skydiver, where the force of the resistance of air is equal to the force of the pull from gravity, we have reached terminal velocity. The way a skydiver positions his or her body—belly down or head down—affects terminal velocity.

Belly facing the ground, more surface area, higher upward force from air resistance. Terminal velocity = ~175–210 kph (~110–130 mph)

divemasterking2000/Wikimedia

Head facing the ground, lower surface area, lower upward force from air resistance. Terminal velocity = upward of 480 kph (~300 mph)

The Force of Gravity

All objects with mass are attracted to each other by a type of force called **gravitational force**. The magnitude of this force depends on the mass of the two objects and the distance between them. When you compare any object on Earth to Earth itself, Earth is by far the larger mass; therefore, it has the larger gravitational force.

Every object has a gravitational force of attraction. There is a gravitational force of attraction between you and a skyscraper, a mountain, a boulder, and even a book. However, you can't quite feel this attraction because the mass of these objects are insignificant when compared to the mass of Earth.

Earth also encounters gravitational forces throughout space. The sun's and moon's gravitational forces significantly affect Earth. Ocean tides occur because of the force of gravity exerted on the ocean by the moon. The moon pulls the ocean toward it as it orbits Earth. This pull causes water levels in certain areas to rise and fall in relation to the moon's orbit.

The sun's large mass creates a gravitational force so strong that it influences the orbits of all the planets in our solar system. So why don't objects on Earth "fall" toward the sun instead of toward Earth? This is because the distance between the objects and Earth is much less than the distance between those objects and the sun.

Acceleration due to Gravity

The force of gravity causes objects to accelerate as they fall. On Earth, the force of gravity causes free-falling objects to accelerate at a constant rate of about 9.8 m/s^2. This is known as **gravitational acceleration (g)**. When the only force acting on a falling object is gravity, that object is said to be in freefall.

Think back to the skydiver who jumped from the helicopter. The skydiver would initially have a velocity of 0 m/s. After one second, the skydiver's velocity would be 9.8 m/s.

The mass of the moon is smaller than Earth's mass. Therefore, the gravitational force of the moon is less than Earth's, which is why astronauts who walk on the moon are able to bounce so high. The gravitational acceleration on the moon is only 1.62 m/s^2.

Weight and Mass

Mass and weight are often confused with each other. **Mass** measures the amount of matter in an object. **Weight** measures the gravitational force exerted on an object. The strength of a gravitational force on an object does not change the object's mass, but it can change its weight.

Check for Understanding

✓ How does gravity affect your daily life?

✓ What is the difference between weight and mass?

Calculating Force & Weight

If you compare the formulas for Newton's Second Law and weight, you will notice that they are similar. This is because weight is a type of force.

Force = mass × acceleration

weight = mass × acceleration (due to gravity)

The difference in an object's weight on Earth and on the moon can then be explained by Newton's Second Law and the difference in gravitational acceleration.

Earth
Force (weight) = 50 kg × 9.8 m/s^2 = 490 N

Moon
Force (weight) = 50 kg × 1.62 m/s^2 = 81 N

Example

Gravitational forces, also known as g-forces, can be felt on a roller coaster. The force of gravity on the surface of Earth is equal to 1 g. Increases in g-force happen in anything moving. Roller coasters are usually designed to be about 3 g's. When the force on you is equal to 0 g, you experience weightlessness.

boris23/Wikimedia Commons

Action and Reaction

Consider the launch of a space shuttle. The shuttle pushes gases downward as it burns fuel. This is the action force. The reaction launches the shuttle upward with an equal force. This upward force will propel the space shuttle skyward into space.

Hedavid/Wikimedia Commons

A hockey player also uses action and reaction forces to skate toward the goal. As the player pushes off with his skates, the blades exert a sideways force on the ice. At that same moment, the ice reacts and exerts an equal force in the opposite direction. These forces work together to move the skater across the ice. The forces exerted by the person's skates and the ice are called action and reaction forces. The skates exert an action force on the ice while the ice reacts and exerts an equal force in the opposite direction.

Fast Fact

Some animals take advantage of action-reaction forces. Birds use Newton's Third Law of Motion to fly. When birds flap their wings, the wings push air downward, causing an equal and opposite reaction that pushes the bird upward. The amount of downward force on the air is equal and opposite to that of the air on the bird.

Ryan Kincade/The JASON Project

Try This!

Pass a 5-meter piece of string through a plastic drinking straw. Tie the ends of the string onto two chairs. Position the chairs so that the string becomes taut. Blow up a balloon; do not tie the end of the balloon, but rather pinch the opening. Carefully tape the balloon onto the straw. Let go of the balloon and observe. How does the balloon demonstrate Newton's Third Law of Motion? Identify the action and reaction forces.

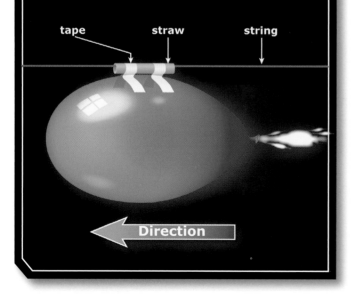

tape   straw   string

Direction

Newton's Third Law

Sir Isaac Newton developed his Third Law of Motion long before space travel was considered a possibility. **Newton's Third Law of Motion** states that for every action force, there is an equal and opposite reaction force. Just like a skater pushing off with his/her blades or a rocket blasting into space, an action force results in a reaction force.

Kobie Boykins needs to consider action and reaction forces while planning the launch of *Curiosity*. Using free-body diagrams, he can map out the forces that act upon *Curiosity*—from the launch here on Earth to the landing on Mars. How much action force do the rockets need to exert to get into space? How much fuel does *Curiosity* need to exert action forces in space to steer it toward Mars? How much force will it take to decelerate *Curiosity* so that it can land safely on Mars? These are just some of the forces Kobie needs to consider for a successful mission.

Check for Understanding

✓ How can Newton's Third Law explain why you move upward when you jump?

Newton's Laws of Motion

When Sir Isaac Newton was alive, space travel would have been considered too far-fetched to even consider. Yet Newton's hard work, dedication, creativity, and that of countless other scientists have paved the way for Kobie Boykins and his team of scientists and engineers. Newton did not develop these laws on his own. He used the ideas of other scientists, including Galileo, Copernicus, and Kepler, as a launching pad to experiment and, ultimately, write his three fundamental laws of the physical universe.

Newton's work was the catalyst for further experimentation and exploration by the scientists that followed him. His three basic laws of motion have led us to manned flight, space exploration, and thousands of inventions that have improved our lives on Earth. Scientific achievements are never made in isolation. Our knowledge and understanding of the universe will continue to progress as scientists like you build upon past ideas.

How fast will this spacecraft accelerate? Apply **Newton's Second Law**:

Force = mass × acceleration

By rearranging this formula, you will find that acceleration depends on the mass of the spacecraft and the force produced by the burning rocket fuel. The greater the mass of the rocket, the more force—and fuel—is needed to move the rocket. That is why every gram counts.

Newton's Third Law says that every action force has an equal but opposite reaction force. As the fuel in the rocket burns, it produces an action force that is directed downward. As the rocket pushes the gas downward, the reaction force causes the rocket to lift off in the opposite direction.

Newton's First Law is the law of inertia. It states that motionless objects will remain motionless, such as the rockets on the platform before launch, and an object in motion will continue moving with the same velocity unless a force changes its motion or direction. That is why it takes a large amount of initial force to get the rockets moving from their motionless state on the launch pad.

DVDShub/Flickr

It's a Blast!

3...2...1...blast off! There is something exciting about watching a rocket launch. In the fall of 2011, Kobie Boykins and his team at JPL will be watching anxiously as the Atlas V 541 launches toward Mars. That's because the rover *Curiosity*, which the team has been working to design and build, will be part of the Atlas' load of about 3,400 kilograms of rockets and other spacecraft.

In this activity, you will create and test rockets to explore the physics of motion, including the effect of mass. From your observations, you will construct an understanding of Newton's Second and Third Laws of motion, as well as the basics of rocket propulsion.

Materials
- Lab 2 Data Sheet
- safety goggles
- 2 film canisters
- construction paper
- scissors
- tape
- balance
- duct tape
- dish pan (for launch tray)
- 50-mL graduated cylinder
- large pitcher of water
- seltzer tablets (1 per group plus extras in case of misfire)
- paper towels

Lab Prep

1. Design and engineer two rockets using a film canister, paper, and tape. One rocket must have a greater mass than the other. To vary the rockets' mass, you can make one rocket larger by enlarging its pieces.

2. Cut out the paper pieces for both of your rockets. Then assemble your rockets with tape, following your design. Make sure that no paper or tape extends around the mouth of the film canisters, and that the canisters seal tightly when the lid is attached.

3. Measure the mass of each rocket (including the film canister and lid) using a balance. Enter the mass (in grams) on your data sheet.

Make Observations

1. Put on your safety goggles. Select one member of your team to measure how high the rockets fly during launch. This person should observe the rockets' flight in reference to the measurement marks on the wall.

2. Put half a seltzer tablet into the canister and then add 15 mL water. Your teacher will quickly cap the film canister and place the rocket on the launch pad.

3. Move away from the launch pad. Then carefully watch the rocket and make observations as it launches.

4. Enter the maximum height of flight, measured in centimeters, on your data sheet.

5. Repeat steps 2–4 for the second rocket.

6. Make a table on your data sheet that contains your data and your classmates' data for the mass and the maximum height of flight.

7. Set up a scatter plot of mass versus maximum height of flight. Place mass on the y-axis. Place maximum height of flight on the x-axis and choose an appropriate scale. Label each axis and give the plot a title.

8. Plot each data point on the graph.

Reflect and Apply

1. During which launch did the rocket go the highest?

2. What factors seemed to affect the maximum height of flight?

3. How did your rocket launches demonstrate Newton's Laws of Motion?

Extension

Complete this activity using varying amounts of seltzer tablets. Compare your graphs. What did you notice?

 Journal Question According to Newton's Third Law, when you kick a soccer ball, it exerts the same force on you as you do on it. Using Newton's Second Law, explain why the soccer ball moves farther than you.

In This Stage:

Your expedition goal is accomplished when you:

Know how forces and fluids interact.

Know how the understanding of fluids helps us navigate our environment.

Why this is important:

Understanding the interaction between forces and fluids can help us improve upon current technology such as sea vessels, airplanes, and space travel.

Words to Identify

fluid, pressure, Pascal's principle, Archimedes' principle, Bernoulli's principle, lift, buoyant force

Stage 3: Dynamic Fluids

What is a Fluid?

Did you know that on Earth, we are always surrounded by a fluid? A **fluid** is a substance that does not have a definite shape and is able to flow. The two most important fluids for life on Earth are air and water. Water flows from your faucet and takes the shape of your cup. Air flows through the atmosphere and fills our lungs with every breath. The fact that we live within a fluid makes it important to understand how forces behave in different fluids.

Despite the fact that fluids do not have a definite shape, they can be very powerful forces. Wind and water can move boulders. And, throughout history, the exploration of forces exerted by fluids has led to many remarkable achievements. Ancient Polynesians colonized many of the Pacific Islands because they mastered the force that air and water exerted on their sea vessels. In 1903, the Wright brothers successfully took to the air by exploring the forces that air exerts on objects.

Kobie Boykins' work is similar to these early explorers because he, too, must learn to navigate through fluids. As *Curiosity* journeys to the surface of Mars, it will travel through many different fluids. It must first escape Earth's atmosphere and travel through the vacuum of space. When *Curiosity* reaches Mars, it must then navigate through the mysterious fluids that make up the Martian atmosphere and safely land on its surface. In order to successfully accomplish this mission, Kobie and his team of engineers must consider and prepare for all the forces that *Curiosity* will encounter.

There are two concepts that are particularly important to understand how forces behave in fluids: pressure and buoyancy. **Pressure**, the amount of force exerted on a specific area, acts differently in a fluid than in a solid. Buoyancy explains the ability of objects to float on liquids.

Check for Understanding

✔ What is a fluid?

✔ What fluids will *Curiosity* encounter on its journey to Mars?

Luis Argerich/Wikimedia Commons

Shalom Jacobovitz/Wikimedia Commons

▲ Surfers ride on the interface between two fluids, the air and the water.

Our Ocean Planet

If you have ever dived to the bottom of a swimming pool, you have felt the pressure that water can exert on your eardrums. The deeper you dive, the more water is on top of you and the more pressure you feel. In the deepest known part of the ocean, the Mariana Trench, the pressure can be as much as 8 tons per square inch (108.6 MPa or 15,751 psi)—the same pressure a person would feel if he or she were trying to hold up fifty jumbo jets.

Most of the oceans on Earth have never been fully explored. One reason for this is that the pressure of the water, or hydrostatic pressure, presents unique challenges to exploring the deep ocean. Scuba divers cannot withstand the pressures any deeper than 100 meters, which is only a small fraction of the ocean's depth. Even in specially built submersible vehicles, humans can only travel about halfway to the bottom of the deepest oceans. The rest of the exploration is left to unmanned remotely operated vehicles (ROVs) designed to withstand the extreme pressures of the deep ocean.

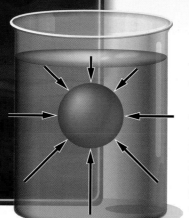

Pressure and Fluids

Along with the changing forces *Curiosity* will encounter on its mission, it will also face changes in pressure. Pressure is closely tied to force as it is the amount of force exerted by a substance on a certain area. Pressure is equal to force divided by area.

Imagine getting your foot stepped on during a soccer game by a player wearing cleats. If this were to happen to you, you would probably get a bad bruise from the impact. Now consider that same player stepping on your foot while wearing regular sneakers. It might hurt, but it would not hurt as much as the cleats. If you take a closer look, the cleats on the bottom on soccer shoes are very narrow. Each cleat has less area than the soles of a sneaker, resulting in a greater amount of pressure exerted. Pressure increases in fluids as well. For example, when you pour a glass of water, the area of the bottom of the glass experiences the pressure of the water above it.

This pressure is equal to the force of the water divided by the area of the bottom of the glass. As the water level rises, so does mass of the water and, therefore, the pressure on the bottom of the glass.

This works similarly to swimming deeper into a pool. As you get deeper, the amount of water above you increases. When this happens, the pressure on your body also increases. On the other hand, as you swim toward the surface, the column of water above you decreases, as does the pressure.

Calculating Pressure

Compare the approximate pressure created by the front half of soccer cleats and the front half of a shoe with a flat bottom from a person weighing 578 newtons (130 pounds).

Area of one cleat = 0.000283 square meters

Let's assume there are 10 cleats on the front half of the shoe. 0.000283 × 10 = 0.00283 square meters

Area of front half of flat bottom shoe = 0.0113 square meters

Pressure from cleats = 578 newtons / 0.00283 square meters = 204,240 N/m^2 (pascals)

Pressure from flat bottom shoe = 578 newtons / 0.0113 square meters = 51,150 N/m^2 (pascals)

The force exerted over a specific area (N/m^2).

pressure = Force / area

Anything, such as a push or pull, that causes a change in the motion of a freely moveable object, or causes stress in a fixed object (N).

The space inside a two-dimensional object (m^2).

Pascal's Principle

Curiosity is not the first mission to explore the surface of Mars. In January 2004, NASA successfully landed two Mars rovers, *Spirit* and *Opportunity*, on the Martian surface. To help cushion their landing and protect sensitive onboard instruments, landing gear was designed using a scientific principle developed more than 300 years ago by a French scientist named Blaise Pascal. **Pascal's principle** states that when a force is applied to an enclosed fluid at any point on the container, there is an equal change in pressure at every other point in that container.

If you were to fill a plastic water bottle with water, the water will exert a force on the entire surface of the bottle. If you squeezed the bottle without the lid on, the water would come squirting out of the top of the bottle. But, if you squeezed the bottle with the lid on, the increase in pressure would be applied equally throughout the bottle.

When developing the rover landing gear, NASA engineers designed giant gas-filled airbags to cushion the impact between the rovers and the Martian terrain. This utilized Pascal's principle, as the airbags exerted an equal pressure on all points in contact with the Mars rover. Therefore, the force of the landing is spread out over the whole area of the Mars rover, rather than just a few points. Since pressure is equal to force divided by area, increasing the area over which the force is applied decreased the pressure on the rover as it landed.

Fast Fact

Generally, the first sign that your body is experiencing changing pressures is felt in your ears. Your eardrums are made of a thin membrane sensitive to pressure changes. You may have felt the effects of changes in pressure in your ears as they "pop" to adjust to the change.

As a passenger on a plane, you may feel a minor change in pressure as the plane flies into the sky. As your altitude increases, the column of air above you decreases, resulting in a drop in pressure. You may also feel a change when the pressure around you increases significantly, such as when a plane lands or you swim in deep water.

Check for Understanding

✓ What is pressure and how does it change with depth?

✓ Describe an application of Pascal's principle.

Equal pressure applied throughout.

Force applied upon landing.

NASA

Why Do Objects Float?

Picture a log floating motionless on the ocean. If the log only encountered the downward force of its weight, it would sink. Therefore, we know there is an upward force exerted by the water. This upward force is called the buoyant force. You can feel this force if you try to press and hold a floating object, such as a beach ball, beneath the water. The buoyant force pushes the object back to the surface.

Any object submerged in a fluid will experience an upward buoyant force regardless of whether it sinks or floats. In the case of the floating log, the buoyant force exerted by the water is equal to or greater than the log's weight so the log will float. However, if the buoyant force is less than the log's weight, then the log will sink.

Archimedes' Principle

Approximately 2,200 years ago, a Greek mathematician named Archimedes developed a method to determine an object's buoyant force. According to **Archimedes' principle**, when an object is placed in a fluid, it will displace the fluid to "make room" for the object. The weight of the displaced fluid is equal to the buoyant force acting on the object.

Gretta Gotsabend/flickr

Picture a glass of water that is filled completely to the top. If someone were to place an ice cube into that glass, what would happen? The ice cube would float but not before some of the water overflowed. Archimedes determined that the weight of the displaced water is equal to the buoyant force exerted on the floating ice cube. Because the buoyant force is greater than weight of the ice cube, the ice cube floats.

Archimedes' experiments with buoyant force led to a better understanding of density and flotation. Archimedes discovered that, in most cases, an object or substance will float if it is placed within a fluid of greater density. If an object or substance is denser than the fluid that surrounds it, the object will tend to sink. Next time you are shopping for groceries, take a walk through the salad dressing aisle. You will notice that certain salad dressings have layers of oil, water, vinegar, and spices. These layers occur because of density differences.

However, some objects that are denser than the fluid they are placed in float. Remember that the weight of the fluid that an object displaces is equal to the buoyant force acting on that object. If the denser object can displace enough fluid to equal its weight, then the object—like a boat—will float.

Gretta Gotsabend/flickr

Team Highlight

Argonaut Aubrey Gonzalez examines an aluminum rod that was pulled apart. Engineers at JPL test materials before they are sent into space to confirm their physical properties. One test is a tensile strength test, where objects are pulled apart until they fail. Engineers then know the limits to which they can design parts for the space vehicles.

MarcusObal/Wikimedia Commons

Try This!

Take two 10 cm × 10 cm pieces of aluminum foil. Shape one into a ball. Shape the other into a boat. Place both objects into a bucket of water. What happens? Why? What forces are acting on your boat? Carefully place paperclips into your boat until it sinks. How many paperclips did it handle? How can you improve your design? Compare your results with classmates. Now, try the same experiment with a piece of clay. Can you make a ball of clay float?

Many boats are made of steel because it is light, strong, and resists corrosion. However, if a block of steel were placed in water, it would sink. Steel sinks because its density is about 7.85 g/cm^3 compared to water's density of 1 g/cm^3. So, how do steel boats float? The hull of a boat is usually shaped like a bowl. The bowl-like shape increases its volume so that it can displace more water than if it were shaped like a block. In fact, the shape is designed to displace enough water so that the **buoyant force** is equal to the boat's weight and carrying capacity.

Bernoulli's Principle

Ships capitalize on Archimedes' principle to stay afloat. But how do planes stay in the air? Planes can fly in part because their design takes advantage of pressure differences. Wings on many planes are designed to apply a principle developed by a Swiss scientist named Daniel Bernoulli. He discovered that when the velocity of air or any fluid increases, pressure decreases. Conversely, if velocity decreases, then pressure increases. This relationship between pressure and velocity is known as **Bernoulli's principle.**

Airplane wings are often designed so that the shape is different on the top and on the bottom of the wing. When a plane flies, the wings cut through the air, and air flows over both the top and the bottom of the wings. However, the air on top of the wing travels faster than the air on the bottom. According to Bernoulli's principle, when the velocity of a fluid increases, pressure decreases. Conversely, if velocity decreases, then pressure increases. The lower pressure on top of the wings relative to the bottom causes an upward force known as **lift**.

The wing also helps to produce lift, based on Newton's Third Law. Air that hits the wing as the plane moves is forced downward. The equal and opposite reaction exerted by the air pushing up on the wings helps provide lift. If the upward force generated by action-reaction **forces** or air pressure differences is greater than the weight of the plane, then the plane will fly.

Check for Understanding

✓ Describe an application of Archimedes' principle.

✓ Describe an application of Bernoulli's principle.

Fast Fact

Curiosity is loaded with specialized state-of-the-art technology, including high-definition cameras, robotic arms, and computers. Supported by sensitive circuitry, these instruments are necessary for gathering and sending information back to Earth. As *Curiosity* travels through space, high energy x-rays emitted by the sun can damage circuitry resulting in instrument malfunction. In order to prevent this from happening, dense materials, such as lead, are used to shield certain areas from the high-energy particles emitted by the sun. These dense materials make it more difficult for x-rays and other rays to pass through.

Mars Science Laboratory – AKA Curiosity

The name *Curiosity* came from Clara Ma, a sixth grade student from Sunflower Elementary in Lenexa, Kansas. It was selected based upon Clara's essay outlining humankind's natural curiosity as the driving force behind exploration and science. This driving force highlights the Mars Science Laboratory's Mission—to investigate the past or present potential of Mars to support microbial life. *Curiosity* will accomplish this mission using state of the art lasers, cameras, collection instruments, and onboard test and analysis chambers, all powered by nuclear energy. The launch date is scheduled for the fall of 2011, and it should arrive on Mars sometime in August 2012.

NASA

Size: Approximately twice as long (2.8 m or 9 feet) and four times as heavy as previous Mars exploration rovers launched in 2003.

Toolkit:
Laser – vaporize rock samples
Sensors – analyze rock and soil to detect organic compounds
Mast-mounted camera – observe distant objects to help mission control navigate exploration targets and driving routes
Arm-mounted camera – observe objects in close proximity
Powdering drill and scoop – drill into rocks and scoop samples from the soil
Deck-mounted instruments – analyze powdered rock and soil samples

Mobility:
Six-wheel drive – can roll over objects 65 cm (25 in.) tall and travel up to 200 m (660 ft) per day

Front and rear wheels – have individual steering motors, allowing for 360-degree turns

Rocker-bogie suspension system

Power: Nuclear battery allowing for year-round operation

Check for Understanding

✓ Describe how Pascal's, Archimedes', and Bernoulli's principles can be applied to your life.

Principles at Work

Pascal's Principle

When a force is applied to an enclosed fluid at any point of the container, there is an equal increase in pressure at every other point in that container. When the same pressure is applied over a larger area, the amount of force is multiplied. This principle is the basis for hydraulic systems.

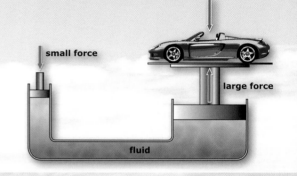

Archimedes' Principle

When an object is submerged in a fluid, it will displace the fluid to "make room" for the object. The weight of the displaced fluid is equal to the buoyant force acting on the object.

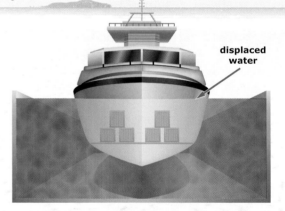

Bernoulli's Principle

When the velocity of a fluid increases, pressure decreases. Conversely, if velocity decreases, then pressure increases.

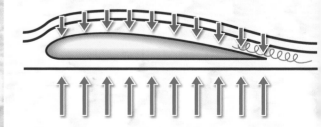

Ryan Kincade/The JASON Project

Cartesian Diver

As *Curiosity* travels to Mars, its spacecraft will travel through fluids in the atmospheres of Earth and Mars. To land *Curiosity* safely on the surface of Mars, Kobie Boykins and his team need to understand how forces such as pressure act in these fluids.

In this activity, you will have the opportunity to explore how some forces behave in fluids. Using an ordinary medicine dropper, you will observe the interaction of pressure, volume, and buoyancy, as you control the depth of an object called a Cartesian diver.

Materials

- **Lab 3 Data Sheet**
- **glass medicine dropper****
- **2 small plastic soda bottles with screw cap; at least twice as tall as the dropper**
- **funnel**
- **bowl**
- **small glass of water**
- **commercial ketchup package**
- **water**
- **sponge (for clean-up)**

** You can use plastic medicine droppers, but you'll need to counteract the buoyancy by adding the extra mass of waterproof modeling clay.

Lab Prep

1. Use the funnel to fill a small soda bottle with water. Stop filling the bottle when the water level is three-fourths full.

2. Fill the medicine dropper three-fourths full of water. Gently drop the medicine dropper into the cup. Adjust the water level in the medicine dropper until it just barely floats when placed in the cup. Then, gently place the dropper into the soda bottle, open end first.

3. Place the bottle over a bowl. Continue filling the bottle until it just overflows. Tighten the screw cap.

4. While holding the container over the bowl, squeeze it firmly. The dropper should float when the bottle is left alone and sink when the bottle is squeezed. If this does not happen, remove the medicine dropper, adjust the level of water in it, and try again.

Make Observations

1. Using a pin or thumbtack, poke about 20 holes near the top of a second small soda bottle.

2. Hold the soda bottle with holes over a large bowl and fill it with water to a point just under the holes. Replace the lid. Slowly squeeze the bottle until water starts to come out of the holes. Record your observations.

3. Place the Cartesian diver on a desktop surface. Observe the glass dropper part of the diver. Can you identify a water line in the dropper? Make a sketch of your observations.

4. Carefully remove the medicine dropper. Then replace the dropper with a ketchup packet. Observe the packet's response as you squeeze and release the container.

Reflect and Apply

1. How does this force from squeezing the bottle affect the water inside the bottle? Explain what you observed in step 4, using Pascal's principle.

2. What happens as you squeeze the bottle? What happens to the amount of water in the dropper? Explain why this happens, using Pascal's principle.

3. The formula for density is density = mass × volume. Did the mass or the volume of the medicine dropper increase when water was forced into the medicine dropper? When pressure was applied to the ketchup packet? Explain.

4. Using Archimedes' principle, explain why the change in mass or volume caused the divers to sink.

 Journal Question Do you think that filling the Cartesian diver bottle with soda water would affect its operation? Explain.

To Infinity and Beyond

Recall that your expedition goal is to *apply your knowledge of forces and Newton's Laws of Motion to explore the universe around you.*

Now that you are fully briefed, it is time to analyze and understand how scientists use this knowledge of forces and motion with respect to land rovers such as *Curiosity* on other planets to explore unknown worlds.

Kobie Boykins and the team of researchers at NASA's Jet Propulsion Laboratory (JPL) are interested in safely landing un-manned rovers on the surface of other planets, such as Mars. They also want to ensure the rover lands in a specified region that they have already selected for exploration. Once a rover has safely landed on the surface, it can then explore this selected area and conduct a series of scientific experiments that will look for signs of life. To ensure the rover lands safely and in the right area, Kobie and the team must consider all of the forces that the spacecraft and rover will experience during the landing phase. Using concepts such as Newton's Laws of Motion, Kobie is constantly developing new and innovative ways to land on the surface while reducing the forces that may damage the rover and any of the delicate instruments aboard.

To begin this Field Assignment, you will analyze a diagram of the entry, descent, and land-

Peter Haydock/The JASON Project

ing phase of the NASA *Curiosity* mission. Using information on this diagram, you will think about all of the forces acting on *Curiosity* to develop free-body diagrams for the different stages of this phase in the mission. Using this knowledge, you will then create a balloon-driven rocket which will attempt to deploy a payload into a specific landing area. Through experimentation and testing, you will make adjustments to improve the design of the rocket and deployment device to increase the accuracy of the landing location.

Materials

- Expedition 3 Field Assignment Data Sheet
- tape measure or meter stick
- fishing Line
- balloons
- soap
- straws
- small metal nuts (2-3)
- 2 chairs
- duct tape
- marker
- materials supplied by your instructor

Objectives:

- Analyze the forces and motion involved in the entry, descent, and landing phases of the Mars *Curiosity* mission.
- Design a balloon rocket which drops a payload safely into a drop zone.
- Analyze the forces and motion of the balloon rocket and payload.
- Conduct tests to analyze the accuracy and precision of the rocket and payload.

Field Prep

1. Read through the *Curiosity* Entry, Descent, and Landing Outline and Diagram.

2. On the diagram, draw a free-body diagram for the following parts of the phase:
   a. Entry Interface
   b. Peak Deceleration
   c. Parachute Deploy
   d. Powered Descent
   e. Skycrane: Touchdown
   f. Flyaway

3. Calculate the acceleration of *Curiosity* between the following stages of the phase:
   a. Entry interface to parachute deploy.
   b. Parachute deploy to heat shield separation.
   c. Heat shield separation to back shell separation.
   d. Back shell separation to rover separation.
   e. Rover separation to touchdown.

4. Describe how each of Newton's Laws applies to different parts of the entry, descent, and landing of the rover.

Expedition Challenge

In the expedition challenge, you and your team will design a spacecraft, which will attempt to deploy a payload in a specified landing area. Your goal is to design a spacecraft and deployment device, which is accurate and precise in the landing area.

1. Build the basic structure of the spacecraft and deployment device according to the directions and diagrams in the data sheet.

2. Set up the testing area by securely taping one end of the fishing line to the back of a chair or wall.

3. Thread the other end of the fishing line through the long straw of the rocket structure.

4. Pull the fishing line taut and securely tape the other end to the back of another chair or an opposite wall. Make sure the rocket moves freely along the fishing line. Increase the tension as needed to make the fishing line as straight as possible.

5. Set up a landing area on the floor with tape or paper as shown in the data sheet.

6. Blow up the balloon and reel up the deployment device before launching.

7. When ready, release the balloon and analyze where the payload first lands on the ground and where it stops. Document your results.

8. Conduct two more trials using this rocket setup and document your results.

9. Adjust your rocket or deployment device as needed to increase the accuracy inside the designated landing area.

10. Conduct three trials for this setup and document your results.

11. Continue adjusting your rocket and deployment device as needed to improve its functionality.

12. Develop recommendations and modify your device to improve its functionality.

Expedition Debrief

1. Make a drawing showing the different stages of the rocket's launch and the deployment and landing of the payload.

2. On the diagram, draw a free-body diagram for each stage.

3. How do each of Newton's Laws apply to different parts of the rocket launch, payload deployment, and landing?

Journal Question Describe how having an understanding of forces and motion helps researchers to develop new designs for things, such as spacecraft, airplanes, cars, or other machines that are put into motion.

Peter Haydock/The JASON Project

Expedition 3: Forces

Continue to explore the concepts and formulas that describe forces by solving the problems on these pages.

Calculating Force

Force is described as an object's mass multiplied by its acceleration.

Sample Problem

Carey pushes a 10 kg shopping cart, causing it to accelerate at 1 m/s². What is the net force acting on the cart?

Understanding the Problem:

What information does the problem give you?

Mass: 10 kg
Acceleration: 1 m/s²

What are you trying to find out?
force

Force =
mass × acceleration (F = ma)

What formula do you need?
F = m × a

> Substitute the known values in the equation.

> Express your answer in newtons (1 N = 1 kg·m/s²).

Solving the Problem

F = ma ▷ **F = 10 kg × 1 m/s²** ▷ **F = 10 kg·m/s²** ▷ **F = 10 N**

> Start with the formula.

> Multiply to solve.

Do not forget to check your problem. Does your answer make sense?

Challenge

The force of gravity between two objects can be calculated using the formula:

M1= Mass of object 1
M2 = Mass of object 2
Fg = G × M1 × M2/r²
Fg = Gravitational Force
r² = Squared distance between mass 1 and mass 2
G =Gravitational constant
(6.6726 x 10¹¹N·m²/kg²)

Calculate the gravitational force between Earth and its moon given that:

Earth's mass = 5.9736 × 10²⁴ kg
The moon's mass = 0.0749 × 10²⁴ kg
The distance between Earth and the moon = 3.84 × 10⁵

Try These

- A tow truck accelerates a 1,500 kg car out of mud patch at 2 m/s². What net force is acting o the car?

- A net force acting on a 0.12 kg hockey puck cause it to accelerate at 5 m/s². What is the net force?

- A net force of 300 N causes a 30 kg cart to accel erate. At what rate will the cart accelerate?

- A net force of 200 N causes a toy car to accelerat at a rate of 14.2 m/s². What is the mass of the car

- During a game of tug of war, team A, with a col lective mass of 246 kg, pulls with a force of 50 N Team B, with a collective mass of 253 kg, pull with a force of 45 N. Explain which team will wi and why. How quickly will the losing team acceler ate toward the middle line?

Calculating Weight

Weight measures the gravitational force exerted on an object

Sample Problem

A girl has a mass of 50 kg. How much does the girl weigh on Earth?

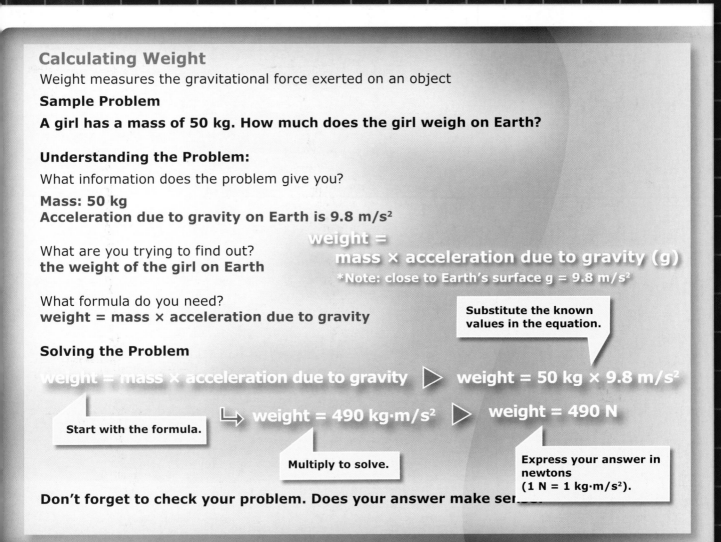

Understanding the Problem:

What information does the problem give you?

Mass: 50 kg
Acceleration due to gravity on Earth is 9.8 m/s²

weight =
mass × acceleration due to gravity (g)
Note: close to Earth's surface g = 9.8 m/s²

What are you trying to find out?
the weight of the girl on Earth

What formula do you need?
weight = mass × acceleration due to gravity

Substitute the known values in the equation.

Solving the Problem

weight = mass × acceleration due to gravity ▷ **weight = 50 kg × 9.8 m/s²**

Start with the formula.

⤷ **weight = 490 kg·m/s²** ▷ **weight = 490 N**

Multiply to solve.

Express your answer in newtons
(1 N = 1 kg·m/s²).

Don't forget to check your problem. Does your answer make sense?

Try These

- A car has a mass of 2,000 kg. How much does it weigh on Earth?

- Suppose a dog with a mass of 20 kg travels to the moon. If acceleration due to gravity on the moon is 1.62 m/s², how much would the dog weigh on the moon?

- Buzz Aldrin and all his moonwalking gear had a mass of 163.6 kg when he walked on the moon. If acceleration due to gravity on the moon is 1.62 m/s², how much less would Buzz Aldrin and his gear weigh on the moon than he did on Earth?

- A single-lane bridge has a maximum weight capacity of 150,000 N. What is the maximum mass of a truck that can travel over this bridge?

- The Mars rover *Curiosity* has a mass of 900 kg. Once on Mars, it will weigh 3,375 N. What is the acceleration due to gravity on Mars?

PHYSICS OF THE CIRCUS

It's the greatest show on Earth—the circus! Have you ever been to the circus? You enter a tent and hear, "Ladies and Gentlemen! Children of all ages!" As the lights come up, in front of you are elephants, lions, dazzling costumes, clowns, and... physics!

Wait a minute...what?

The circus—with its trapeze artists, acrobats, tight rope walkers, the human cannonball, and even clowns—all rely on forces and motion to dazzle and amaze the audience. We're not trying to say that your teacher is a clown, but we are saying that the very concepts your teacher teaches in class are the same concepts used by the circus performers.

The Human Cannonball

Human cannonballs have been around since the 1870s when "The Great Farini" (William Hunt of Port Hope, Ontario) developed the technology to launch a human projectile. Later, a new cannon was created, this time powered by compressed air. This act, performed by the Zacchini family, came to America from Europe by John Ringling, of the Ringling Circus. The Zacchini's were launched from cannons several thousand times, sometimes reaching speeds around 90 miles per hour. Over the years, the act evolved to include the men being fired over the top of a Ferris wheel.

On May 29, 1998, the Guinness Book of World Records recorded a new record with a shot of 56.64 m (185 ft, 10 in.), by David "Cannonball" Smith, Sr. (the same day, his son, David "The Bullet" Smith, Jr. completed a shot of 55.19 m (181ft, 10 in.). So, how do these human cannonballs do it? Newton's Second Law states:

Force = mass × acceleration

StephanieSmith/Wikimedia Commons

When a man is launched from a cannon, the compressed air gives him a large acceleration. This, when combined with the man's mass, leads to a very large force. The acceleration of being shot from a cannon pushes the man into the air until an outside force (gravity and air resistance) is greater than the acceleration. With careful aim (and practice!) the human cannonball lands safely in a net.

That Flying Trapeze

In the mid-19th century, circus crowds were dazzled—and terrified—by a new circus act: the flying trapeze. The act was invented by a French teenager, Jules Leotard. Leotard created the first trapeze over his father's swimming pool in 1859. He took his death-defying act to the Cirque Napoleon, where he quickly became a sensation throughout Europe.

Though modern trapeze tricks may be different and even more daring, the basic physics behind the trapeze hasn't changed since Leotard first took to the air. What gives the trapeze artist the ability to soar so far with such speed? Momentum. Behind the somersaults and gasp-inducing last-minute grabs of the trapeze act, lies an idea familiar to most kids on the playground. If you jump off as you swing, you will fly through the air—much further than if you just jumped. Trapeze artists use the momentum of their swing to increase their velocity when they let go. How does this work?

momentum = mass × velocity

AlejandroLinaresGarcia/Wikimedia Commons

Picture the act that allows the trapeze artist to soar furthest through the air: the swinging platform. In this act, two trapeze artists swing on a metal platform, high above the circus ring. One artist then launches herself through the air to be caught by another person hanging from a trapeze. Consider this act as a closed system including the swing, the two trapeze artists on the swing, and the "catcher" and his trapeze. The law of conservation of momentum tells us that the momentum in this system can't be lost, only transferred.

As the two artists swing together, they have a combined momentum equal to their combined mass, plus the mass of the swing, multiplied by their velocity. That is a lot of momentum! As the flyer jumps from the swing, she carries some of that momentum with her. Her mass once she leaves the swing is much less than the combined mass of both artists and the swing. Since her mass has decreased, her velocity must increase in order to conserve momentum. In addition, when the flyer pushes off the platform, she gets an extra boost of momentum from that push. To conserve momentum, the velocity of the platform actually changes directions, giving it momentum in the opposite direction.

All this momentum from the system, transferred to the flyer's relatively small mass, increases her velocity, allowing her to soar further through the air. When the catcher catches the flyer, her momentum is combined with his. Her momentum was greater than his, so they continue to move in the direction she was moving. However, since their combined mass is larger than hers was alone, their velocity decreases and they slow down.

Juggling

Have you ever tried to juggle? Throwing one object up and catching it is simple. Doing this with two objects at the same time is a bit trickier. The more objects you try to juggle, the more difficult it gets.

Though the talented jugglers that perform in the circus can do tricks like juggling blindfolded or while riding a unicycle, there is a limit to how many pins they can juggle while simply standing in one place. In fact, the record for juggling pins is only eight pins at a time! The reason? You guessed it—physics.

Juggling involves projectile motion. Consider all the forces acting on a pin as it arcs from one of the juggler's hands to the other. First, there is the upward and horizontal force exerted on the pin by the juggler throwing it. Then there is the inertia that causes the pin to keep moving in the same direction even after the juggler's force stops acting on it. Eventually, the force of gravity overtakes the inertia, causing the pin to start accelerating toward the ground. Finally, there may be some air resistance that slows the pin down and might even cause it to move from side to side. When you think about all the forces at play, juggling even three pins starts to seem pretty amazing.

All falling objects at the same elevation accelerate at the same rate due to gravity. In order to have time to catch one pin before the next one falls, the juggler's initial force must send each pin a little higher than the one before. Because the rate of acceleration is the same, the further a pin falls, the faster it is going. So to keep the pins from landing too close together, not only does a juggler have to throw the next pin higher than the one before, but that height increases with each new pin. Eventually, a juggler will come to a point where he can't throw any higher or a point where he is throwing so high that he can't throw as accurately. This will determine the number of pins he can juggle.

hbp_pix/flickr

crystal/flickr

J Baylor Roberts and Donald McBain NGS

JongleurSpanien/Wikimedia Commons

YOUR TURN

Use your knowledge of forces and motion to come up with your own circus act. Keep it safe by keeping everything on the ground, and present your idea to your teacher before you try it. Your class can combine acts to create a physics circus and introduce some simple physics concepts to a younger class.

Make It Work
Work, Power, and Machines

"As time went on and we learned more about the extent of the spill and the time it was going to take to control it, I knew that my life and my work as a scientist had permanently changed."

—Lisa Jones
Marine Biologist, NOAA

Lisa Jones

Prepare for your expedition by viewing this briefing on your objectives. Learn how Lisa Jones and the other scientists at NOAA use simple and complex machines as they monitor and clean up the Gulf region in the aftermath of the Deepwater Horizon oil spill.

Meet the Researcher Video
Join Lisa Jones as she monitors seafood in the Gulf region for safety. Explore the simple and complex machines found on the ships and in other tools used by Lisa and the scientists at NOAA.

Biologist, National Marine Fisheries Service, NOAA

Read more about Lisa online in the JASON Expedition Center.

Peter Haydock/The JASON Project

Photo Credits (left to right): jcgoforth/flickr; USCG; alvimann/morgueFile; Peter Haydock/The JASON Project; Peter Haydock/The JASON Project

Your Expedition Goal...

Evaluate the technological and societal applications of work, power, and machines.

To accomplish your expedition goal successfully, you will need to

- Distinguish the scientific definitions of work, power, and energy from their "everyday" definitions.

- Calculate work, power, and mechanical advantage in a variety of real-life situations.

- Identify the six simple machines and analyze their roles in performing work.

- Illustrate the differences among pulleys.

- Use efficiency and mechanical advantage to describe the function of machines.

- Distinguish simple machines from complex/compound machines.

Join the Team

Join the Argonauts as they study the effects of the Deep Horizon oil spill that occurred in the Gulf of Mexico. Marcelo Ancira, Kendra Elie, Maggy Botros, and Marty Kelsey went to Pascagoula, MS, to work with Host Researcher Lisa Jones from NOAA's National Marine Fisheries Service. Lisa works on monitoring marine life for oil contamination. The Argonauts met many of Lisa's colleagues who work on conservation and preservation challenges in the Gulf. As part of their work, the Argonauts studied and used many simple and complex machines on the NOAA ships and boats to collect samples for testing.

After the Spill

At 9:45 a.m. on April 20, 2010, the Deepwater Horizon oil rig, situated in the waters off the Gulf of Mexico near Louisiana, exploded, killing 11 workers. Oil began leaking immediately after the explosion. Over the next three months, the leak released as many as 67,000 barrels of oil per day into the Gulf of Mexico. As news of the spill began to trickle in, National Oceanic and Atmospheric Administration (NOAA) biologist Lisa Jones knew that her life and her work would never be the same.

As a biologist at NOAA's National Marine Fisheries Service in Pascagoula, Mississippi, Lisa Jones monitors populations of aquatic animals in the Gulf of Mexico. Following the Deepwater Horizon spill, Lisa Jones and her fellow biologists have increased their efforts to catch and test seafood species for contaminants and to monitor their populations. Lisa's work helps to ensure that seafood from the Gulf is safe to eat and that various populations remain stable, so that commercial fishermen, and others who depend on these creatures for their livelihood, can begin to recover economically.

Lisa is part of an enormous team of engineers, sailors, fishermen, scientists, and others who have worked to stop the spill and protect both the Gulf ecosystem and the livelihood of the people whose lives depend upon it. From capping the well, to cleaning the oil out of the water and wetlands, to ensuring the region is safe, this impressive team effort has involved over 47,000 people.

Like others in this large and complex team, Lisa Jones uses machines every day. Powerful engines drive the trawling boats that Lisa uses to catch and monitor bottom-dwelling sea creatures such as shrimp. The boat's propeller uses a simple machine called a screw. Another simple machine, a pulley, makes it possible for Lisa to lower heavy equipment into the water.

In order to create and maintain the kind of equipment that makes it possible for Lisa Jones to catch and monitor sea creatures, scientists must understand how simple machines function and how to combine them to perform complex tasks. Understanding concepts such as work, power, mechanical advantage, and efficiency helps scientists develop machines that will efficiently do the work that scientists, like Lisa, can't do on their own.

Expedition 4 Briefing Video Prepare for your expedition by viewing this briefing on your objectives. Learn how scientists such as Lisa Jones, use simple and complex machines to explore, investigate, and protect our world.

In This Stage:

Your expedition goal is accomplished when you:

Can calculate the work done on an object.

Can calculate the rate at which work is done.

Why this is important:

Work, power, and energy help us make increasingly more efficient machines that improve our quality of life and advance technology.

Words to Identify
work, energy, law of conservation of energy, joule, watt, horsepower

Expedition Briefing

Stage 1: Let's Get to Work!

Are You Working?

You have rushed up the stairs and sat down just in time to hear the bell ring. You pick up your pencil and look to the front of the room for your practice problems. Today's problems are especially tricky. You get halfway through the first problem and realize you forgot to carry the one. You go back and erase everything you have done and start all over.

In this scenario, would you say you have done some **work**? At what point? Was the math problem work? How about climbing up the stairs? What about moving the pencil? Erasing your mistakes? As we explore the scientific definition of work, you might be surprised by which of these do and do not count as work.

NOAA / Wikimedia Commons

Calculating Work

Work is equal to the force multiplied by the distance over which the force is exerted. With that in mind, can you answer the following?

A 500-N force is applied to a 50 kg box to push it 10 m across the deck of a research boat. How much work was done?

work = 500 N × 10 m

Five thousand joules of work were done as the box was pushed across the desk.

Measured in joules (J).

Distance over which force is exerted, measured in meters (m).

work = Force × distance

Anything, such as a push or pull, that causes a change in the motion of a freely moveable object, or that causes stress in a fixed object, measured in newtons (N).

What Works

One of the trickiest things about science is that scientists often have very specific meanings for words we use every day. "Work" is one of those words. When you talk about work, you may be referring to cleaning your room, your parents' careers, or a problem on your math test. These are all perfectly acceptable ways to talk about work in day-to-day conversations. Scientifically speaking, however, work means one thing, and one thing only.

Work is the product of a force being exerted over a certain distance. When you push your pencil across the page, you are doing work because you are applying a force to move the pencil over a distance. Climbing the stairs is also work, since you had to apply force to move your body up the stairs. Thinking about the math problem was not work in scientific terms, though it may have felt like work to you.

A concept closely related to work is **energy**. This is another term you are probably very familiar with, which has a specific meaning in science. Energy is the ability to do work. Energy can be transferred or transformed into different forms, but in a closed system where no outside influences interfere, it is never created nor destroyed. This observation is called the **law of conservation of energy**. The fact that energy is conserved will be important to keep in mind as we learn more about work.

To understand the very specific way work is used in physics, it is worth investigating what qualifies as work and what does not. The mathematical definition defines work as force multiplied by distance. What happens if you multiply any number by zero? The product is then zero. Therefore, if zero distance or zero force is involved, the total amount of work is zero. In other words, no work has been done.

Example

Suppose you exert an upward force on a window to open it. As you exert the force, the window moves. You did work. Now suppose the next window is locked. Even though you try to push the window up, exerting as much force as you did on the first window, the window does not move at all. Even though you exerted the same force, you did not do work because the window do not move.

Try This!

Play "work charades" with a small group of classmates. Without talking, mimic a simple action. The other members of your group should identify the action and decide whether or not it meets the scientific definition of work.

ardelfin/morgueFile

When determining the amount of work that has been performed, the following should be kept in mind:

- **Work has to include motion.** In order for work to be performed, an object has to move some distance. Suppose a trawling net used by Lisa Jones and her team becomes stuck, and no matter how hard they pull, it does not move. Lisa and her team might feel tired, but no work has been done.

- **Only force in the same direction as the object's motion counts as work.** A person pulling a wagon is exerting an upward force as well as a forward force. However, only the forward force is used to calculate work, since the wagon moves forward, not upward.

- **Only the distance an object moves while a force is being applied counts as work.** If, for example, you pushed a toy truck and it drove across the table, the work you did occurred only during the initial shove. You would not take into account the total distance traveled by the truck when calculating work. Once you stop pushing the truck, inertia causes it to keep moving, so no more work is being done on it.

Check for Understanding

✓ How are work and energy related?

✓ Why doesn't studying for a test meet the scientific definition of work?

Joules

Remember that force is measured in newtons (N) and distance is measured in meters (m). This means that moving one newton over 1 meter is equal to one unit of work, one newton meter (Nm). Another name for the newton meter, in fact, the preferred name, is the **joule**. One joule is equivalent to one Nm.

Try This!

Look at the images below. One person is walking down the hall holding books; the other is carrying books up stairs. In one case, the person's arms are not doing work on the books. In which photo are the person's arms NOT doing work on the books? Draw a force diagram to help you see the answer, and discuss your answer with a classmate.

Ryan Kincade/The JASON Project

Is it Work?

Example	Is a force exerted?	Is the force moving over a distance?	Is it work?
Holding something up over your head.	Yes, upward.	No	No
Lifting something over your head.	Yes, upward.	Yes	Yes
Opening a door	Yes, outward.	Yes	Yes
Pulling a wagon	Yes, upward and forward.	Yes	Yes, the part moving the wagon forward.

Calculating Power

Power is equal to the work divided by the time over which the work is exerted. With that in mind, answer the following:

5,000 J of work are done on a 50 kg box to push it 10 m across the deck of a research boat in 50 seconds. Calculate the power.

power = 5,000 J / 50 s

power = 100 W

Now calculate the power if 5,000 joules of work are done on the same 50 kg box to push it 10 m across the deck of a research boat in 25 seconds.

power = 5,000 J / 25 s

power = 200 W

Measured in watts.

Force (in newtons) × distance (in meters) (in joules).

power = work / time

The time during which work is done (in seconds).

The Key to True Power

If you walked up a flight of stairs, and then later ran up a flight of stairs, would you be doing the same amount of work? You would, because the force (equal to your body's weight) and distance (the length of the block) would be identical, whether you walked or ran. However, running around the block means you would do the work much faster. From a practical standpoint, engineers typically want to know more than simply whether work is being done on an object. They want to know the rate at which work is being done.

Power

Power describes the rate at which work is done, or the rate at which energy is transformed. Power is calculated by dividing work by the time it takes to do that work.

The metric unit for power is the **watt** (W). You might have heard this term used to describe electrical appliances such as light bulbs or hair dryers. For very large and very small measurements of watts, the standard metric prefixes are used. For instance, the power used in a house is probably measured in kilowatts, and the power used by a large city like Sydney, Australia, is measured in megawatts or even gigawatts.

How many watts are there in a megawatt? How about a gigawatt? Use the chart on page 18 to determine the answer.

Another common unit for measuring power is the **horsepower** (hp). In the United States, horsepower is still used to measure the power of large motors, such as those found in cars or in the fishing boats used by Lisa Jones and her team at NOAA. One hp is equivalent to about 750 W. The horsepower, however, is not part of the International System of Units.

Check for Understanding

✓ Provide an example that demonstrates how two things can perform the same amount of work yet have a different amount of power.

jeltovski/morgueFile

Work

What do you think of when you hear the word *work*? Perhaps a household chore or an afterschool job comes to mind? To scientists like Lisa Jones, work has to do with the energy added to an object. It can be calculated by multiplying the applied force by the distance through which it acts. Mathematically stated, work = Force × distance.

In this activity, you will have the opportunity to explore the concepts of work and power. You will use a spring scale to take vertical and horizontal measurements, and make observations about force, work, and power.

Materials
- Lab 1 Data Sheet
- spring scale
- meter stick
- string
- stopwatch
- masking tape
- variety of objects, without wheels, including large bolts, and books

Lab Prep

1. Examine the spring scale you will be using. What are the units displayed by the scale?

2. Attach an object to the scale and read the force (in newtons) exerted by the object. You may need to calculate the force by converting the mass in grams into a kilogram equivalent. Determine the downward force of this mass using the equation: Force = mass × gravity, with gravity equal to 9.8 m/s^2.

Make Observations

1. Lay the meter stick down on a table or desk. Place the first object at 0 cm on the meter stick. Attach the spring scale to the object and drag it 1 meter across the desk or table.

2. As you are moving the object, take two measurements: time and force. Use the stopwatch to measure and record the time it takes to move the object (in seconds). Record the force (in newtons) from the scale as you move the object.

3. Calculate and record the amount of work (in joules) performed on the object. Use the formula: work = Force × distance.

4. Calculate and record the power (in watts) used to move the object. Use the formula: power = work / time.

5. Repeat steps 1–4 using the same object, but this time, pull the object at a faster rate. What do you observe?

6. Repeat steps 1–5, using at least two additional objects. What differs in each trial? What stays the same?

7. Tape the meter stick in a vertical position against a desk or table. Place the first object on the floor by the meter stick. Attach the spring scale to the object and lift it 1 meter straight up.

8. As you are lifting the object, take the same two measurements you took in step 2. Calculate work and power as described in steps 3 and 4.

9. Repeat steps 7 and 8, using the same object, but lifting at a faster rate. What do you observe? How does this compare with your observations in step 5?

Reflect and Apply

1. How did the force required to pull an object across the table compare to the force required to lift the object?

2. Based on your observations, which factors had the biggest impact on the amount of force needed to move an object? Explain.

Extension

Brainstorm one or more ways to reduce the force needed to lift or pull the objects you tested. With permission, create and test one of your ideas.

Journal Question What factor would you change in order to enable you to do the same work with less force?

In This Stage:

Your expedition goal is accomplished when you:

Know the six types of simple machines.

Understand how machines make work easier.

Why this is important:

Machines increase the quality of human life.

The solutions to the technological challenges of the future rely on machines.

Words to Identify

machine, input force, output force, load, mechanical advantage, efficiency, simple machine, inclined plane, friction, wedge, screw, lever, fulcrum, first-class lever, second-class lever, third-class lever, wheel and axle, pulley, fixed pulley, moveable pulley

Stage 2: There has to be an easier way!

Getting the Job Done

When Lisa Jones goes into the field to sample a species' population, she catches fish. The job seems fairly simple; yet without the help of machines, Lisa would be unable to do it. From the simple machines used to lower and raise fishing nets from her research vessel to the complex engines that drive the boat, machines are an important part of Lisa's work.

Lisa depends on machines, both simple and complex, to study aquatic populations and determine the safety of those populations in the wake of the Deepwater Horizon oil spill. Understanding concepts such as work, power, mechanical advantage, and efficiency allows engineers to design and maintain machines that do the work that Lisa Jones needs to perform. But, Lisa is not the only one who relies on machines. If you like sports, playing music, gardening, eating, or just getting around, machines are an important part of your life, too.

When you hear the term machine, what do you think of? A zamboni? A sonic oscillator? A chainsaw? When do you think the first machine was invented? 50 years ago? 150 years ago? How about 1,000 years ago?

"**Machine**" is yet another word that has a very specific meaning in physics. A machine is any device that completes a task and makes work easier. Using this definition, the first recorded use of a machine was 2.6 million years ago by our ancestors, *Homo habilis*, in modern day Tanzania. *Homo habilis* is Latin for "handy man" because the remains of these early hominids are often accompanied by simple machines: stone tools used to sharpen, chisel, and pierce.

input force

output force

Making Work Easier

How do machines make work easier? Remember that in physics, work is done by forces acting on objects. Machines will change the force's size, direction, distance, or a combination of these in order to make work easier. In a practical sense, machines not only make work easier; they make work possible.

You use machines on a daily basis. For instance, imagine cutting a watermelon, moving a pile of mulch across a yard, or riding a skateboard. To accomplish these tasks, you may use a knife, wheelbarrow, or ramp. These are all types of machines. Let us analyze an example in detail to get a better idea of the components of a very simple machine.

Imagine you are trying to get the lid off of a paint can. It would be impossible for most people to do this without the use of a simple machine. Most people would use a screwdriver to pry the lid off the can. The force your hand applies on a screwdriver as you push down is called the input force. The **input force** is the force you apply onto the machine to get it to do what you want it to do. The screwdriver, in turn, will push up on the lid. The force the screwdriver exerts on the lid is called the **output force**, the force the machine exerts on the object you wish to do work on. The object you are doing work on, the paint can lid in this example, is called the load.

skidrd/flickr

When you apply an input force to the screwdriver to open a paint can, you are applying a relatively small force over a longer distance. By comparison, the output force of the screwdriver to the lid is stronger, but acts over a much shorter distance. So as you push down on the screwdriver's handle, you are moving that handle over a large distance compared to the other end of the screwdriver, which only moves a small distance in opening the can.

Machines allow us to make a trade-off between force and distance. We can increase the total distance while decreasing the amount of force, or we can increase the amount of force to decrease the distance. In either trade-off, the amount of work done remains the same.

As you learn about machines, it is important to note that machines make work easier, but they will not reduce the total amount of work. Machines only change the amount of force used, the direction of the force, or the distance over which that force is exerted. Also remember that according to the law of conservation of energy, energy is neither created nor destroyed. Therefore, the work you put into a machine is the maximum amount of work you will get out of the machine.

Simple Machines and Efficiency

Not all machines are created equally. Machines work in different ways to make work easier, and some machines make work easier than others. Some machines multiply force, some change the direction we need to administer force, and others give us a wider range of motion. Some machines are less wasteful in their conversion of work than others. One way to better understand how much a machine helps in making work easier is by understanding the machine's **mechanical advantage**. The mechanical advantage of a machine tells you the number of times the input force is multiplied by the machine. You can find the mechanical advantage of a machine by dividing its output force by the input force.

The mechanical advantage of a machine is a simple number, but that simple number tells us a lot about how the machine makes work easier. By examining if the number is greater than, equal to, or less than one, a scientist or engineer can tell a lot about whether that particular machines will be useful in solving the problem she is working on. As we go on to examine the various types of machines, we will also analyze their mechanical advantage.

Check for Understanding

✓ How do machines make work easier?

Though a simple tool, a tire iron is actually made up of two simple machines—a lever and a wheel and axle. The lever end is used to pry the rim from the tire. The opposite end contains a socket wrench used as a wheel and axle to turn the bolts holding the tire in place. ▶

Calculating Mechanical Advantage

The overall mechanical advantage of a machine is equal to the output force divided by the input force. With that in mind, can you answer the following?

If the input force of a machine, such as a car jack, is 1,000 N and the output force is 2,000 N, what is the mechanical advantage of this machine?

**mechanical advantage =
            2,000 N / 1,000 N**

The mechanical advantage of this machine is 2.

Expressed as a number.

**mechanical advantage =
    output force / input force**

Force a machine applies to an object to do work on it; measured in newtons (N).

Force applied to a machine to get it to do work; measured in newtons (N).

Calculating Efficiency

Efficiency can be calculated by dividing the output force of the machine by the input force and then multiplying by 100%. Multiplying by 100% helps to express the number as a percentage. With that in mind, answer the following:

Determine the efficiency of a machine, such as a ski lift, which puts out 1,000 J of work when 2,000 J are put into it.

efficiency = (1,000 J / 2,000 J) × 100%

The efficiency of the machine is 50%.

Expressed as a percentage.

Work done by a machine; measured in joules (J).

efficiency = (output work / input work) × 100%

Energy put into a machine; measured in joules (J).

Efficiency

Machines can reduce the force required to perform work, increasing the distance over which that force is applied, but they will never increase the amount of work performed. Why not? Remember the law of conservation of energy states that the ability to do work—energy—can neither be created nor destroyed. However, work output will always be less than work input. This is because some amount of work gets transformed into other types of energy, such as the thermal energy that results from friction. That is, the machine wastes some of the energy you have put into it because the machine has to overcome friction.

To determine how much energy is wasted, a machine's **efficiency** can be calculated. Efficiency is a measure of how close the machine's output is to its input. Efficiency is expressed as a percentage: the higher the percentage of efficiency, the more efficient the machine.

Can you think of why it would be impossible to have a 100% efficient machine?

Simple Machines

Simple machines are devices that will do work with only one movement. There are six types of simple machines: **inclined plane, wedge, screw, lever, wheel and axle,** and **pulley.** Even the most cutting-edge machines used by Lisa Jones and her colleagues can be broken down into different components of simple machines.

Check for Understanding

✓ What do efficiency and mechanical advantage tell us about machines?

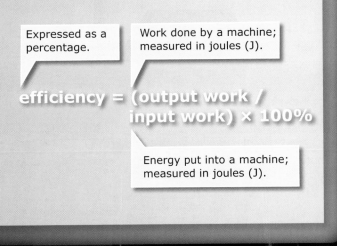

▲ Simple machines can even be found on the ski slopes. Most ski lifts operate as a pulley, powered by a wheel and axle that keeps the pulley moving.

John Picken/flickr

Try This!

Examine the room around you. Identify at least one example of each type of simple machine: inclined plane, wedge, lever, pulley, wheel and axle, and screw.

Six Types of Simple Machines

Simple machines make our lives easier every day, and they are essential to the work done by Lisa Jones and the other scientists at NOAA. We see examples of simple machines all around us. The mechanical advantage of each type of simple machine can be found using a simple formula.

click/morgueFile

Inclined Planes

An inclined plane is any straight, slanted surface. A ramp is a common example of an inclined plane. Inclined planes make work easier by decreasing force but increasing distance.

Imagine you need to move a 1,000 N sofa onto a truck that is 1 meter high. This will take 1,000 J of work. If you lifted the sofa straight into the truck, you would need 1,000 N of force all at once to do 1,000 J of work.

If you carried the sofa up a 5-meter long ramp to a height of 1 meter instead, you would only need 200 N of force to do the same 1,000 J of work. By using an inclined plane, you still have to do a total of 1,000 J of work on the sofa. The inclined plane increases the distance over which you have to exert force to move the sofa. Because work is force multiplied by the distance over which it is exerted, by increasing the distance, the inclined plane decreases the force you need to exert to do the same work.

Mechanical Advantage of Inclined Planes

To calculate the mechanical advantage of an inclined plane, compare how long it is to how high it is.

MA inclined plane = length / height

Inclined planes have no moving parts, but they are not 100% efficient. The surface of the inclined plane, as well the surface of the object being worked on, will have many tiny grooves and bumps. These may be unseen by the naked eye, but are present on all surfaces. Those groves and bumps rub up against each other to produce friction. Thus, some work will always be lost to overcome friction. Using lubricants, such as oil, or trying to find the smoothest surfaces possible can reduce friction and increase the inclined plane's efficiency.

muyra/morgueFile

Wedge

A wedge is a double-inclined plane that moves. Knives, your front teeth, and certain types of doorstops are all great examples of wedges. A wood splitting maul is another example of a wedge. If you think about how a maul splits wood, you can understand how wedges make work easier. When the input force is applied along the flat, blunt edge of the wedge, it gets transferred to the inclined edges of the wedge, where the output force is directed outward, or perpendicular. This change in direction of the force is why when you hit a maul with a hammer on the top blunt edge, the input force is redirected outward, pushing the wood apart in a direction perpendicular to the input force.

Mechanical Advantage of Wedges

The mechanical advantage of a wedge can be increased by making the wedge longer and thinner. The mechanical advantage of the wedge is then calculated by dividing the length of the sloped edge by the wedge at its greatest thickness. This is why blades need to be sharpened. Sharpening makes the thin end of the blade even smaller, increasing the ratio between the length of the slope and the width.

mechanical advantage of wedge = length of slope / width at largest end

Like the inclined plane, wedges have no moving parts. However, wedges will never work at 100 percent efficiency because some work is lost to overcome the friction caused when surfaces rub against each other.

Mike Schmid/flickr

Wheel and Axle

A wheel and axle is a simple machine made of two circular or cylindrical objects of different sizes, fastened together and moving around a common axis. When you picture a wheel and axle, you probably picture something like a bicycle wheel or a ferris wheel. But, screwdrivers, wrenches, doorknobs, and steering wheels all use a wheel and axle.

Technically, the wheel and axle is a type of modified first-class lever, but it is so common and so useful that the wheel and axle is considered to be its own category of simple machine.

Mechanical Advantage of Wheel and Axle

The mechanical advantage of a wheel and axle is typically greater than 1. Force can be applied to the larger circle (wheel) which acts on the smaller cylinder (axle). Because the second cylinder is smaller, force is required to act over a smaller distance and is therefore magnified. As you know by now, this makes work easier.

Force can also be applied to the axle, which then acts on the wheel, allowing the force to be applied over a longer distance. For example, you apply a larger force to the axle of a pizza cutter, which then allows the wheel of the pizza cutter to apply a smaller force over a longer distance. Ferris wheels are also wheel and axle machines in which the force is applied to the axle, causing the large wheel to turn over a greater distance.

Mechanical advantage of a wheel and axle is found using the following formula:

MA of wheel and axle= radius of the wheel (R)/radius of the axle (r)

Mattes/Wikimedia Commons

Pulley

A **pulley** is a grooved wheel with a rope (or cable or chain) running through the groove. Pulleys are used in elevators, some window blinds, and flag poles. To use a pulley, you pull on one end of the rope (input force). At the other end of the rope, the output force pulls on the object you want to move. There are two basic types of pulleys: fixed and moveable.

Fixed Pulley - If a pulley is attached to a structure and only changes the direction the force is moving, it is a **fixed pulley**.

Moveable Pulley - A **moveable pulley** is attached to the object you are trying to lift. It decreases the amount of force needed to move the object by increasing the distance over which the force is applied

Complex pulley systems, made up of more than one pulley, can be used to lift extremely large and heavy objects.

Mechanical Advantage of Pulleys

Mechanical advantage in pulleys is calculated by counting the total number of sections of rope supporting the load. When calculating the mechanical advantage of a pulley, only the sections supporting the load are counted; the section of rope being pulled down is not.

By definition, all fixed pulleys have a mechanical advantage of 1, because they do not change the force or distance of the work being done, only the direction. A single moveable pulley always has a mechanical advantage of 2.

Screw

Screws are inclined planes wrapped in a spiral. Screws can be used to fasten things together, hold things together, or apply force to an object. You can find screws in jars, nails, bolts, monkey wrenches, vices, and of course, screws. The screw on the bottom of a light bulb allows the light bulb to both be connected securely to a fixture and also easily removed.

Mechanical Advantage of Screws

In order to determine the mechanical advantage of a screw, the length of the inclined plane wrapped around the screw is measured and divided by the length of the cylinder it is wrapped around.

MA screw = length of inclined plane/length of cylinder

The mechanical advantage of a screw can also be estimated; screws with a greater mechanical advantage will have more threads that are tightly wrapped and closer together.

Check for Understanding

Describe some inclined planes you might see around your school. Provide evidence that these are in fact inclined planes.

Why does sharpening a knife increase the mechanical advantage of a wedge?

▲ A sail on a ship is lowered and raised by a pulley system on the mast.

Levers

If you've ever played on a seesaw at the playground, or used a fishing pole, a rake, a baseball bat, or even your own elbow, you have used a lever. Levers are very common simple machines. A lever consists of a rigid bar that pivots or rotates at a fixed point.

The fixed point that the lever pivots or rotates around is called a **fulcrum**. Levers make work easier because they increase the output force, change the direction of the input force, or increase the distance over which a force is applied. The arrangement of the fulcrum, input, and output forces on a lever can change. These various arrangements define whether a lever is classified as a first-, second-, or third-class lever. Each class of lever performs work in very different ways.

Mechanical Advantage of Levers

The mechanical advantage of levers depends on where the fulcrum is located. The equation for mechanical advantage of levers is as follows:

MA of levers = distance from fulcrum to input force / distance from fulcrum to the output force

Since each class of lever has a different location for the fulcrum, input force, and output force, each class has a different mechanical advantage.

FIRST-CLASS LEVER

First-class levers all have their fulcrum between input and output forces. Examples of first class levers include seesaws and elbows. Because the distances between the components of a lever can vary, the mechanical advantage of first-class levers can be either one, less than one, or greater than one.

Example: Crowbar

How it works: The fulcrum is closer to the load than it is to the input force. This means that the input force acts over a greater distance, magnifying the force, creating a larger output force.

Mechanical Advantage: Greater than 1 (will magnify the input force)

input force

output force

fulcrum

Example: Seesaw

How it works: Fulcrum is halfway between the load and input force. Force is not magnified, but direction of force is changed.

Mechanical Advantage: Equal to 1 (will only change direction)

dancerinthedark/morgueFile

Example: Rowboat

How it works: With the fulcrum closer to the input, you can enact a force over a greater distance, but the input force will need to be greater than the output force.

Mechanical Advantage: Less than 1 (will decrease the input force)

mckaysavage/flickr

SECOND-CLASS LEVER

Second-class levers have their output force between the input force and the fulcrum. By definition, the input force is always farther away from the fulcrum than the output force, which means that second-class levers will always have a mechanical advantage greater than 1. Second class levers always multiply force, making work easier because they allow less force to be exerted on the load, in exchange for acting over a greater distance. Unlike first-class levers, second-class levers do not change the direction of the input force.

A wheelbarrow is a second-class lever. Heavy items placed in the wheelbarrow are the load. The axle is the fulcrum, and the force is applied at the handles. When you lift the handles, you apply less force than would be needed to directly lift the load. However, you apply that force over a greater distance as you lift the handles further than the load is lifted.

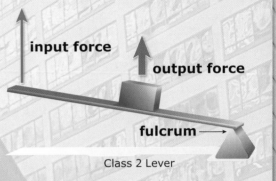

Class 2 Lever

Examples: Wheelbarrow, nut-cracker

How it helps to do work: Magnifies force

THIRD-CLASS LEVER

Third-class levers are levers that have an input force between the output force and a fulcrum. Third class levers, by definition, will have a mechanical advantage that is less than 1. This means they decrease the force originally put into the machine. Unlike first class levers, third-class levers do not change the direction of the force, either. Third-class levers are useful because they increase the distance over which the output force is exerted.

For example, a broom is a third-class lever. When you sweep, you exert force over a short distance as you move the handle. On the other end of the lever, the boom head moves with less force over a much greater distance, allowing you to sweep up objects from a bigger area.

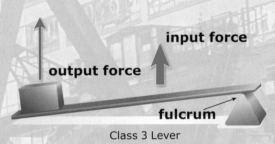

Class 3 Lever

Examples: Fishing pole, hammer, rake

How it helps to do work: Increases distance

▲ A draw bridge is a large lever that functions by counterbalancing weights. Underneath the bridge is a large weight—a room filled with tons of concrete block. To raise the bridge, the weighted room is lowered, causing the other end of the lever—the bridge itself—to lift up. When the room is raised again, the bridge lowers, similar to what happens to a seesaw when one person gets off.

b0jangles/flickr

Machines and Mechanical Advantage

The mechanical advantage of a machine indicates how many times the machine will multiply the input force. If a machine has a mechanical advantage greater than 1, that machine will increase the input force. However, not all machines increase the input force. If a machine has a mechanical advantage of 1, the input force and output force of the machine are the same. In this case, the machine will provide another advantage, such as a change in direction. Finally, if a machine has a mechanical advantage of less than 1, that machine will actually decrease the input force. Since a machine doesn't change the amount of work being done, if the input force is decreased, the distance in which the force is applied is increased.

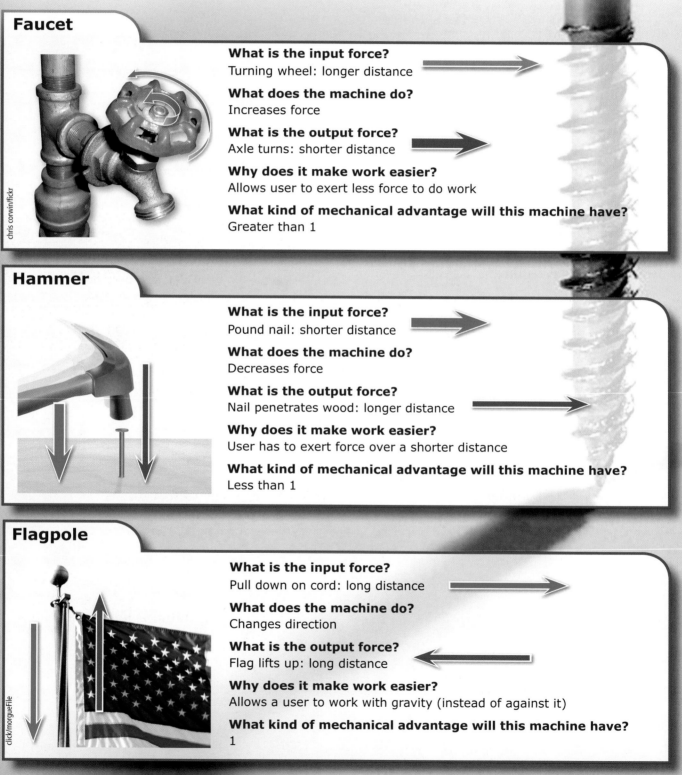

Faucet

chris corwin/flickr

What is the input force?
Turning wheel: longer distance

What does the machine do?
Increases force

What is the output force?
Axle turns: shorter distance

Why does it make work easier?
Allows user to exert less force to do work

What kind of mechanical advantage will this machine have?
Greater than 1

Hammer

What is the input force?
Pound nail: shorter distance

What does the machine do?
Decreases force

What is the output force?
Nail penetrates wood: longer distance

Why does it make work easier?
User has to exert force over a shorter distance

What kind of mechanical advantage will this machine have?
Less than 1

Flagpole

click/morgueFile

What is the input force?
Pull down on cord: long distance

What does the machine do?
Changes direction

What is the output force?
Flag lifts up: long distance

Why does it make work easier?
Allows a user to work with gravity (instead of against it)

What kind of mechanical advantage will this machine have?
1

Ella's Dad/flickr

Simple Machines

Look around you. In a matter of minutes, you could probably find examples of the six simple machines that form the basis for many of the tools that we use to make our lives easier. Can you spot a pulley? A lever? An inclined plane? What about a wedge, a screw, or a wheel and axle? Common objects such as knifes, ramps, and shovels are examples of simple machines that help us do work more easily.

In this lab, you will examine each type of simple machine and perform experiments to identify how these machines help you do work more easily.

Materials
- Lab 2 Data Sheet
- materials provided by instructor

Lab Prep

1. When you enter the laboratory, do not touch any of the stations. Wait for instructions from your instructor before beginning the lab.

2. With your instructor, review all appropriate laboratory procedures, safety guidelines, and classroom rules.

3. Review the objectives and any procedures that are established for each station.

4. Review the order in which you will move from station to station.

5. Familiarize yourself with how to use a spring scale if you have not used one before.

Make Observations

1. After your instructor has presented the lab prep, a signal will be given to begin work at your first station. Remember that you only have a limited time to work at each station and answer questions.

2. Use the tools and materials that are available at that station to perform the suggested investigations.

3. At each station, follow the instructions and record your observations on the data sheet.

Reflect and Apply

Answer the following questions at each station:

1. Did the amount of work change with and without the machine? Explain.

2. Does it seem easier to do the same amount of work using the simple machine? Why?

3. Work is equal to force times distance. When using the machine, how is the input force and distance over which it acted different from the force and distance needed to do the work without the machine?

4. How is the machine's output force and the distance over which it acted different from the input force and distance over which it acted?

5. How did changing the mechanical advantage of the simple machine affect your ability to perform the task?

Extension

Come up with a way to combine two simple machines to complete a task. Draw or describe your idea and present it to the teacher. After getting your teacher's approval, create the device and use it to complete a task. Determine a way to measure the amount of work done with and without the machine.

Journal Question How would you expect the distance to change if the force is increased, assuming the same amount of work is being done? Describe the relationship between the force and the distance needed to do work.

Our Ocean Planet

The Deepwater Horizon leak occurred many miles offshore and more than 1,500 meters beneath the ocean's surface. However, scientists are concerned about its long-term impact on sensitive coastal regions called estuaries. Thousands of species of fish, shellfish, and other plants and animals spend some part of their lives in the mangroves, bayous, oyster reefs, and other habitats found in estuaries. Estuaries in the Gulf region are vital to commercial fishing and recreational activities that bring tourists to the area. As oil from the leak moves into estuaries, scientists from NOAA and other organizations are working to protect the many species and habitats that make estuaries so important.

United States Coast Guard

U.S. Army Environmental Command/flickr

Workers and volunteers used a variety of tools to remove oil that made it to shore. All workers and volunteers had to be trained in safe techniques before working near the oil spill.

USFWS/Southeast/flickr

Trained wildlife rehabilitation experts and veterinarians, many of them volunteers, worked to capture and treat wildlife affected by the oil spill.

John Masson/USCG

On the morning of the Deepwater Horizon explosion, rescue workers with helicopters searched for and helped move survivors to safety.

Stephen Lehmann/USCG

Helicopters and planes flew over the spill area directing skimmers and booms to areas with major oil slicks. Aircraft also helped to monitor wildlife, map the location and size of the spill area, and other monitoring tasks.

Booms along coast

Controlled burn

NOAA research vessel

Vessel of Opportunity

Oil slick

Booms sprea[d] by shrimp bo[at]

Containment booms are used to keep approaching oil slicks away from shorelines and wetlands. Rough waters, weather, and other factors can sometimes allow oil to get past the booms.

One method for removing oil from the surface of the water is controlled burns. Booms are used to concentrate oil, which is then set on fire and allowed to burn off the water.

Containment booms are floating barriers made from inexpensive materials that help to capture and trap oil on the surface of the water. Booms can be used with skimmers to concentrate oil for skimming. More than 13 million feet of boom have been used in Gulf oil cleanup efforts.

Remotely-operated vehicles or ROVs played a large role in detecting and stopping the leak at the Maconda well. Because it is difficult and dangerous for humans to work under the pressure and cold conditions in the deep sea, engineers had to rely on ROVs to do all the mechanical labor to fix the leak.

Patrick Nichols/U.S. Navy

Justin Stumberg/U.S. Navy

Gary Rives/USCG

USCG C-Innovation   DEEPWATER HORIZON BOP

USCG

Transocean/USCG

Patrick Kelley/USCG

Barry Bena/USCG

In the aftermath of the Deepwater Horizon explosion on April 20, 2010, coast guard fire boats attempted to put out the fires on the burning rig. In the first days, efforts were focused on rescuing survivors and putting out fires. The leak was not discovered by remotely-operated submersible vehicles until April 24.

In June, a temporary containment cap was placed on the blowout preventer. This enabled some of the leaking oil to be pumped onto the Discoverer Enterprise instead of into the Gulf. Since the ship had a limit to how much oil it could hold, the oil was burned in controlled flares.

The Helix Q4000 vessel performed a number of jobs during the three-month effort to stop the leak. It served as the staging vessel for the attempts to stop the leak by inserting heavy drilling mud and old tires, golf balls, and other junk into the blowout preventer.

Development Driller III was used to drill a relief well to divert the oil from the original well. Drilling of two relief wells began in May 2010, but took several months to complete. The relief wells were finished in September, and by September 19, the well was considered permanently sealed.

Skimmer

Helix Q4000

ROV vessel

Discoverer Enterprise

Development Driller III

Underwater oil plumes

Remote operated submersible vehicle

Macondo well and failed blowout preventer

Relief well

In This Stage:

Your expedition goal is accomplished when you:

Know what compound machines are.

Can describe how compound machines help us in our everyday lives.

Why this is important:

When we can identify natural examples of simple and complex compound machines, we can imitate the same concepts in other areas of our life, and use the concepts to help us. Even "simple" concepts can help us solve the most complex problems.

Words to identify

compound machine, block and tackle, pulley system

Stage 3: Man versus Machine

What is a Compound Machine?

Once a machine involves more than one simple machine, that machine can no longer be considered simple itself. Machines that are made up of two or more simple machines are called **compound machines**, or complex machines. Most machines you've encountered are compound machines. You just learned that a pulley is a simple machine. If you combine two pulleys together, or a pulley and another simple machine, you have created a compound machine.

Pulleys can be combined in a number of ways. You can add several pulleys together to form a **pulley system**. A very common pulley system is one that includes a fixed pulley—to change the direction of your force—with a moveable pulley to magnify your force. Such a pulley system is often referred to as a "**block and tackle**."

Compound machines have been used since ancient times, and you do not have to look too far outside of your classroom to find them! A wheelbarrow is a compound machine that includes a lever and a wheel and axle. A shovel is also a compound machine and is made up of a lever formed from the handle and the wedge that digs into the ground.

Your bike is a compound machine that is even more complex than a wheelbarrow or shovel. The wheels are wheel and axle machines, the pedals are levers, the chain system is a pulley, and screws hold the whole thing together. Other machines, such as cars, boats, and computers, are even more complex. As you might suspect, the overall mechanical advantage of a compound machine is going to be influenced by the mechanical advantages of the simple machines that comprise it.

The more components a compound machine has, the more moving parts it has. This means the compound machine is vulnerable to losing efficiency due to friction. One danger with such machines is that they generate so much friction that they can overheat. This is where using low-friction surfaces or lubricants such as oil become important for the safety and care of the machine.

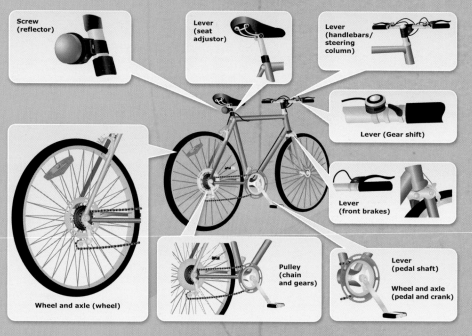

Screw (reflector)

Lever (seat adjustor)

Lever (handlebars/ steering column)

Lever (Gear shift)

Lever (front brakes)

Wheel and axle (wheel)

Pulley (chain and gears)

Lever (pedal shaft)

Wheel and axle (pedal and crank)

▲ A bicycle is a compound machine. In fact, almost every type of simple machine can be found in a bicycle. Levers are used to crank the wheels, change the gears, and engage the brakes. Screws are used to hold parts of the bicycle together. The rear wheel and the pedal and crank that turn it are examples of wheel and axle machines, while the chain that runs between them is a pulley.

Complex Machines in Use

If you analyzed all of the specialized equipment used to cap the Deepwater Horizon spill, clean up the oil, and test the waters in the Gulf, you would likely see various pulleys, wheels and axles, wedges, screws, and more, working together in order to execute extremely sophisticated tasks.

Check for Understanding

✓ How would you determine the mechanical advantage of a pulley system?

Machines in the Human Body

Machines are not simply cold metal tools. Some are made of flesh and bone. As you chew on an apple, pick up a pen, or kick a soccer ball, you are using several machines. We can find a number of simple machines in our bodies. Below is a list of some of the simple machines you can find in our bodies.

If you think about the mechanical advantage of each of these simple machines, you will notice that the design of the human body favors range of motion over force amplification. Why do you think our bodies evolved that way?

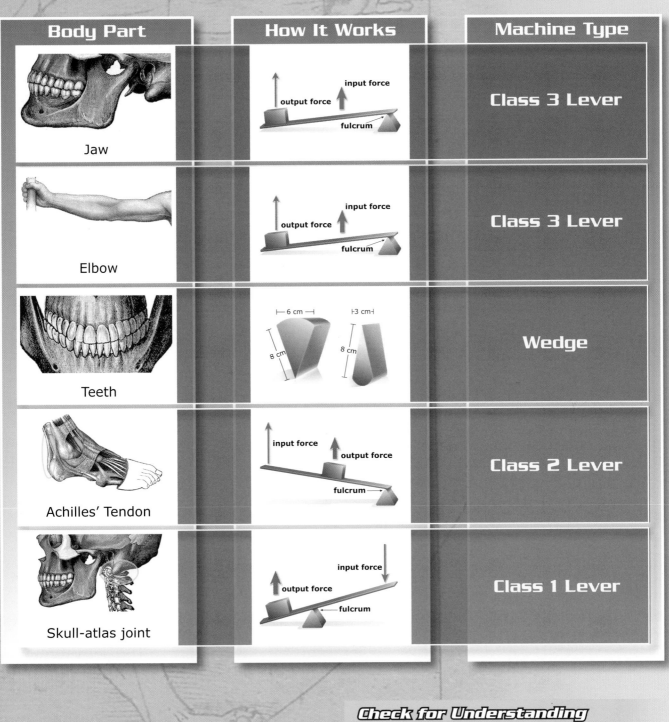

Body Part	How It Works	Machine Type
Jaw	input force, output force, fulcrum	Class 3 Lever
Elbow	input force, output force, fulcrum	Class 3 Lever
Teeth	6 cm, 8 cm, 3 cm, 8 cm	Wedge
Achilles' Tendon	input force, output force, fulcrum	Class 2 Lever
Skull-atlas joint	input force, output force, fulcrum	Class 1 Lever

Check for Understanding

✓ What are some other simple machines found in the human body?

NOAA Research Vessel: *Gordon Gunter*

The *Gordon Gunter* is a NOAA research vessel used by scientists like Lisa Jones and the National Marine Fisheries Service to monitor marine populations. The *Gordon Gunter* is equipped with machines to sample aquatic animals and with research labs in which scientists can study the samples. Lisa Jones and her team use the *Gordon Gunter* to survey marine species for population changes and contamination in the wake of the Deepwater Horizon oil spill.

Pulleys are used to move objects aboard the ship and to raise and lower objects from the ship to the water. By pulling over a longer distance, crew members can decrease the force they need to lift heavy objects.

Winches are wheel and axles that are used to release the trawling net and reel it back in as needed. As the net is wound around the reel, or axle, the diameter of the reel becomes larger. As the diameter grows, it becomes easier and easier to reel in the net.

Cranes are used on the *Gordon Gunter* to load supplies and heavy equipment, such as remotely-operated submersible vehicles or monitoring buoys. Cranes are complex machines, made up of levers, pulleys, and wheels and axles.

GORDON GUNTER

The trawl ramp on the *Gordon Gunter* is an inclined plane. The crew uses the inclined plane to make loading a heavy, full trawling net easier for the crew. The net is hauled a longer distance up the inclined plane, rather than a shorter distance straight up into the ship. Since the work is done over a longer distance, less force is needed to move the net into the ship.

The *Gordon Gunter* is a NOAA research vessel which has six designated lab spaces for scientis To aid the researchers' work, a conveyor belt moves specimens from the trawl deck into the wet lab, for further study.

NOAA Ship Gordon Gunter

The NOAA Ship *Gordon Gunter* serves the National Marine Fisheries Service (NMFS) from the Pascagoula Laboratory in Pascagoula, Mississippi. Operating in Gulf of Mexico, Atlantic Ocean, and Caribbean Sea, the ship is used for many scientific missions including monitoring of deep-water species found in the Gulf of Mexico that are found in the oil spill affected waters. Originally built as the U.S. Naval Ship *RELENTLESS* she was transferred to NOAA in 1993 and recommissioned as the NOAA Ship *Gordon Gunter*. The ship is fitted with modern navigation electronics and oceanographic winches, scientific sampling and sensing equipment, and an observation and survey station for marine mammals.

- Length (LOA): 68.3 m (224 ft)
- Breadth (moulded): 13.1 m (43 ft)

Speed & Endurance
- Cruising Speed: 9.5 knots
- Range: 8,000 nmi
- Endurance: 30 days

Berthing Capacity
- Single Staterooms: 19
- Double Staterooms: 8
- Total Bunks: 35

Complement
- Commissioned Officers: 4
- Crew: 10
- Scientists: 15 (Max)

The amount of force needed to directly close the extremely heavy door to the hydraulics room would make it very difficult for most people to shut the door. Using a lever, crew members can trade force for distance. By using the lever to apply force over a longer distance, the crew can shut the door without needing to exert large amounts of force.

Even the bow of the ship is a simple machine! The ship's bow is made of two inclined planes forming a wedge. Much like an ax cuts through wood, the wedge shape of the ship's bow reduces the force the ship needs to cut through the water, by increasing the distance over which that force is applied.

Man vs. Machine

Machines have been critical to the development of human society. In order for technology to move forward and solve the problems of tomorrow, you and your generation will need to be able to analyze and understand the everyday technologies we take for granted. Remember, even things like scissors were someone's breakthrough ideas sometime in the past. Will you pioneer machines that will improve the lives of children 100 years from now?

Check for Understanding

✔ How have machines influenced human society?

George Washington University Earthquake Simulator "Shake Table"

At The George Washington University (GWU) Northern Virginia Technology Campus, the earthquake simulator is used by researchers and students to study the effects of earthquakes on structures with the main goal of developing new methods to save lives and protect property. The "Shake Table" is a 3 meter (10 ft) by 3 meter (10 ft) table that can shake, rotate, and twist objects in any combination of directions. Whether shaking models up or down, side to side, forward to back, or even rotating and rocking, the researchers at GWU can simulate how structures like buildings and bridges would react in an earthquake or under other stresses.

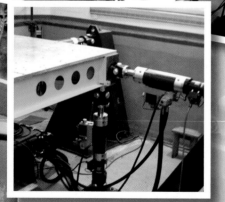

The machine is controlled by a computer program that can simulate past earthquakes or be programmed with anticipated earthquakes. The computer's programming regulates a series of hydraulic controls which shake the table and the model structures attached to it. Forces of up to 80 kilonewtons (18,000 pounds) can be applied to the table to shake the models.

The research staff has tested designs for bridges and even tested buildings made out of locally available materials, including used tires, to see how the structures withstand earthquakes. The machine can also simulate forces from wind, waves, and even vibrations that can lead to materials fatigue.

Additionally, soil behavior can be studied. This table is used to study how soils undergo liquefaction as the result of an earthquake. The integrity of soils used as foundations, or even in dams, can be studied with the table.

GWU researchers use this machine to perform computer simulations to help building and structural engineers design structures that are more resilient to the effects of earthquakes. All of this is done in order to help people stay safe against natural or manmade forces in action.

▶ Researchers Dr. Majid Manzari and Dr. Pedro Silva from The George Washington University run an earthquake simulation using the data from 2010 Chilean earthquake. Components up to 6 meters (20 feet) tall can be tested on the table.

Photos: Peter Haydock/The JASON Project

Complex Machines

Flip on a switch. Turn a door knob. Open a can. Like many of your everyday actions, these processes involve some sort of simple or complex machines. There is no getting around them. Life without the manufactured devices that offer all sorts of mechanical assists, would be unthinkable.

In this activity, you will be challenged to explore an assortment of machines. You will apply critical thinking skills and hands-on inquiry as you move from station to station. Progressing through the series of stations, you will construct a richer understanding of machines and their properties.

Materials
- Lab 3 Data Sheet
- paper and pencil for sketching
- materials provided by instructor

Lab Prep

1. When you enter the laboratory, do not touch any of the stations. Wait for instructions from your instructor before beginning the lab.

2. With your instructor, review all appropriate laboratory procedures, safety guidelines, and classroom rules.

3. Review the objectives and any procedures that are established for each station.

4. Review the order in which you will move from station to station.

Make Observations

1. After your instructor has presented the lab prep, a signal will be given to begin work at your first station. Remember that you only have a limited time to work at each station and answer questions.

2. Use the tools and materials that are available at that station to perform the suggested investigations.

3. At each station, sketch the machine you see. Then identify many of the simple machines utilized to create this complex machine. Label them on your sketch.

Reflect and Apply

Answer the following questions at each station.

1. Based on your observations, is the machine simple or complex?

2. How do the various simple machines work together to help the complex machine to function?

3. What purpose does the machine serve? Does it increase force? Distance? Change direction?

Extension

Gather some old machines, such as mechanical toys, old phones, vacuum cleaners, and so forth, and a variety of tools. Take the machines apart piece by piece, observing how each piece fits with the others. Identify as many simple machines as you can within the complex machine.

 Journal Question Describe a situation where a job was easier because of simple or complex machines

alvimann/morgueFile

David Spender/flickr

Man vs. Machine

Recall that your expedition goal is to *evaluate the technological and societal applications of work, power, and machines*. Now that you are fully briefed, it is time to analyze and understand how machines can help us perform tasks within scientific research.

Using a variety of machines, researchers at NOAA's National Marine Fisheries Service are interested in monitoring the populations of aquatic animals in the Gulf of Mexico. After the Deepwater Horizon oil rig leaked millions of barrels of oil into the gulf, teams of researchers have been working to monitor and test seafood for contaminants so that it is safe to eat. As part of the monitoring, many of these teams depend on a variety of machines to collect information on different forms of plants and animals in the Gulf. One of the machines these researchers use is an underwater ROV (remotely-operated vehicle). In order to move this very heavy, but delicate piece of machinery, they depend on a variety of other machines to get it between locations without harming the expensive devices onboard.

To begin this Field Assignment, you will watch a video of the Argonauts and NOAA researchers using machines to move the ROV. Using this video, you will analyze the variety of simple and complex machines that are involved in the movement of this research tool. Through your analysis, you will determine how different types of simple and complex machines can be used to move delicate tools. Using this knowledge, you will then create a device which will move a delicate object from one location to another. And like the Argonauts, your machine will utilize a variety of simple and complex machines. Through experimentation and testing, you will then make recommendations for ways to improve the design of the machine to make the device even safer for the materials being transported.

Peter Haydock/The JASON Project

Materials
- **Expedition 4 Field Assignment Data Sheet**
- **bar of soap**
- **tape**
- **marker**
- **materials supplied by your instructor**
- **computer with internet access**

Objectives:

- Watch the ROV transport video.
- Identify and describe the simple and complex machines within the video that are involved in the transport of the ROV.
- Design and construct a device, using simple and complex machines, that can safely move a delicate object.
- Experiment with and test your devices functionality.
- Develop recommendations for improving your device's design to increase functionality.

sglickman/flickr

Field Prep

1. Watch the video of the Argonauts transporting the ROV.

2. From the video footage, identify and describe as many simple and complex machines that are used to transport the ROV.

3. Create and label a drawing illustrating each machine.

4. Describe some ways each of the machines makes moving the ROV easier.

Expedition Challenge

In the expedition challenge, you and your team will use a variety of materials provided by your instructor to develop a device which can move a bar of soap from a designated spot on the floor to a table top without damaging or leaving marks in the soap. Your team's device is required to use at least 3 of the following simple machines:

- Inclined Plane
- Wedge
- Screw
- Lever
- Wheel and Axle
- Pulley

1. With your team, brainstorm some different ideas for your device.

2. Develop a blueprint drawing of the design your group decides upon.

3. Using the blueprint and materials provided by your instructor, build your device to move the soap.

4. Test your device to determine its effectiveness in transporting the soap without damage. If your machine leaves marks in the soap, run the soap under water to smooth out the surface and then dry it for the next test.

5. Develop recommendations and modify your device to improve its functionality.

Expedition Debrief

1. Describe each of the simple and complex machines used in your device. Label each on your blueprint drawing.

2. Describe the mechanical advantage that each simple and complex machine provides within your device.

 Journal Question Describe some ways simple and complex machines can help scientists conduct research in a variety of situations.

Peter Haydock/The JASON Project

Expedition 4: Work and Machines

Continue to explore the concepts and formulas that describe work and machines by solving the problems on these pages.

Calculating Work

Work is the product of a force being moved over a certain distance.

Sample Problem

Karen lifts her sister, who weighs 100 newtons, 3 meters to a seat on the top of the bleachers. How much work does Karen do?

Understanding the Problem:

What information does the problem give you?
Force: 100 N (lifting at a constant speed, it takes a force equal to an object's weight to lift it)

Distance: 3 meters

work = Force × distance

What are you trying to find out?
the amount of work that was done

What formula do you need?
work = Force × distance

Solving the Problem

work = Force × distance ▷ **work = 100 N × 3 m** ▷ **work = 300 N·m**

↳ work = 300 J

> Start with the formula.

> Substitute the known values in the equation.

> Express your answer in Joules (1 J = 1 N·m).

> Multiply to solve.

Do not forget to check your problem. Does your answer make sense?

Try These

- Kirstin pushes a wheelbarrow using a horizontal force of 200 N. If Kirstin pushes the wheelbarrow 20 m to the garden, how much work does she do?

- Marcelo tries to move a heavy desk by himself. He pushes with a force of 100 N, but the desk does not move. How much work does Marcelo do?

- Rico pulls a loaded wagon 5 meters with an upward force of 20 N and a forward force of 80 N. How much work is being done?

- Dominic does 53 J of work to move a chair 4 meters. How much force does he exert on the chair?

- Karen has a sprained wrist and can't apply much force to lift a heavy box. There are two machines that she can use. Machine A can do 4,800 J of work over 3 meters. Machine B can do 4,800 J of work over 5 meters. Explain which machine should she use and why.

marioanima/flickr

Calculating Power

Power is the rate at which work is done.

Sample Problem

Gabriel did 100 J of work in 5 seconds. How much power did he use?

Understanding the Problem:

What information does the problem give you?

Work: 100 J
Time: 5 seconds

What are you trying to find out?
How much work was done

power = work / time

What formula do you need?
power = w / t

Solving the Problem

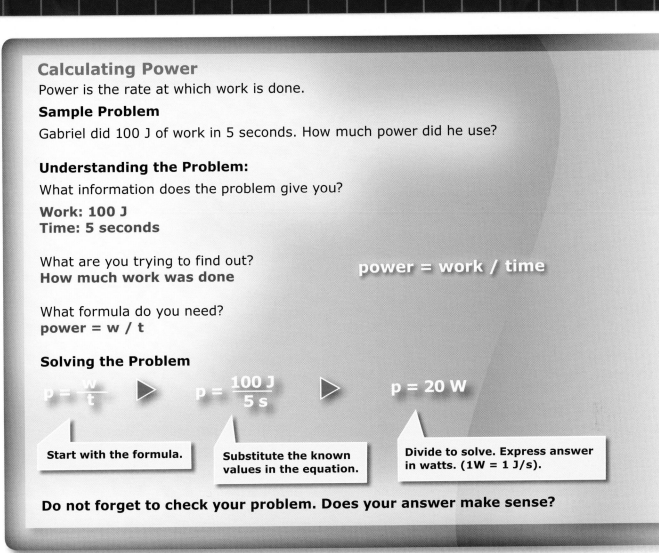

$$p = \frac{w}{t}$$

▶

$$p = \frac{100\ J}{5\ s}$$

▶

$$p = 20\ W$$

Start with the formula.

Substitute the known values in the equation.

Divide to solve. Express answer in watts. (1W = 1 J/s).

Do not forget to check your problem. Does your answer make sense?

Try These

- A machine did 50,000 J of work in 8 seconds. How much power did it use?

- John helped haul rocks for a new exhibit at the nature center. He did 1,200 J of work in 6 seconds. How much power did he use?

- Sara used 400 W of power to do work over 12 seconds. How much work did she do?

- Earnest exerted 950 N of force over 12 meters to move a crate. If it took him 2 minutes to move the crate, how much power did he use?

- Alex has only 30 minutes to unload items from a moving van before it starts raining. If the unloading will require 4,600 J of work and Alex uses 5 W of power, will she finish unloading before the rain begins? Explain.

Lauren Manning/flickr

The Renaissance Man:
Leonardo da Vinci

Can you solve this riddle?

What do the Mona Lisa, a tank, a helicopter, the painting called Last Supper, and details of how the optic nerves work have in common?

Give up?

They were all drawn or painted by Leonardo da Vinci!

Chances are, you have heard of Leonardo da Vinci as a famous 15th century Italian painter. It is true that da Vinci's paintings, particularly the Mona Lisa and the Last Supper, are considered masterpieces, and that da Vinci is respected as one of the greatest artists of all time.

However, saying that da Vinci was a painter is like saying that a rainbow is red—while true, there is much more to da Vinci than just his art. Leonardo da Vinci is an excellent example of a "Renaissance Man."

This term is used to refer to someone who excels in several, very different, fields. For example, in addition to being a master artist, da Vinci was also an inventor, an engineer, an expert on human anatomy, a musician, a botanist, and one of the first known scientists to use methods similar to modern scientific method.

At the root of da Vinci's many accomplishments lies one fact: da Vinci was unceasingly curious. To satisfy his curiosity about the world around him, da Vinci did something that was fairly unusual in the 15th century: he made detailed, systematic observations. Today that may seem like an obvious first step in science. You probably learned to make observations in your kindergarten science class. But in da Vinici's time, gathering empirical evidence was far more rare.

Despite his fame as a painter, fewer than twenty of da Vinci's paintings are known to have survived the 500 years since his death. On the other hand, a number of da Vinci's journals have survived. In these journals, da Vinci made thousands of drawings as he studied areas of interest to him.

Getting to know da Vinci

- Da Vinci was born April 15, 1452, in Vinci, Italy.

- Thousands of people line up at the Louvre in Paris, France each day to view da Vinci's painting, the Mona Lisa.

- In his journals, da Vinci wrote in "mirror writing," from right to left instead of left to right.

- More than 13,000 pages of da Vinci's notebooks and journals still exist. Many are on display in museums around the world.

- Da Vinci worked as a military engineer for the Duke of Milan, designing the catapult, a giant cross-bow, and other war machines.

- Even as a painter, da Vinci was inventive. He often experimented with different pigments and mediums.

- Da Vinci died in France, where he spent his last years as good friend to King Francis I.

Léonard de Serres/Wikimedia Commons

grafixar/morgueFile

For example, to satisfy his curiosity about the inner workings of the human body, da Vinci conducted autopsies. He filled a human brain with hot wax to better see it, attached strings to bones to see how they moved, and drew detailed drawings of what he saw. He drew pages and pages of the same subject, such as the human eye, exploring it from different angles. Some of his drawings are "zoomed in" while others take a wider view. By exploring a subject from many different perspectives, da Vinci could better understand it.

The human body wasn't the only machine that captured da Vinci's interest. Da Vinci studied existing 15th century machines, such as the water wheel, and made detailed drawings of how they worked. In these drawings and the explanations that accompanied them, da Vinci explored the various parts of these machines and how they worked together to accomplish a task. Then, da Vinci did something unusual. He combined the working parts he observed to invent new machines—some of which were centuries ahead of their time.

Among the amazing machines that da Vinci designed on paper so long ago were the helicopter, the tank, an underwater breathing apparatus, and a new kind of bridge. Inspired by his studies of birds, da Vinci designed a number of different flying machines.

Most of da Vinci's designs were never built during his lifetime. Because da Vinci never actually published most of his scientific studies and drawings of inventions, many of his ideas were lost. Centuries later, some of his inventions became reality, thought up anew by modern inventors. The first helicopter capable of carrying a person wasn't built until 1907. The first tank wasn't used until 1917. Jacque Cousteau invented scuba gear that allowed a person to breathe underwater in 1943. In 2001, a bridge based on a design by da Vinci was built in Norway.

Erik Möller/Wikimedia Commons

Da Vinci was truly a "Renaissance Man" whose curiosity, talent, and inventiveness were centuries ahead of his time. Admired both during his life and in the 500 years since his death, da Vinci's contributions to art and science were, well, genius!

YOUR TURN

Select a machine, and spend ten to fifteen minutes examining it and how it works.

Sketch the various parts and how they interact. If possible, take the machine apart and sketch its inner workings.

dorne/morgueFile

Machines on Expedition

Dr. Bob Ballard committed himself to working for 30 years in a deep diving submersible. His goal was to explore, discover, and chart the geologic features of the bottom of the ocean. He wanted proof that the theory of plate tectonics was at work, spreading the ocean crust apart along the mid-ocean ridge in the middle of the Atlantic Ocean.

Since the average depth of the ocean is 4,267 m (14,000 ft), he would start each day at 6 a.m. in the submersible, *Alvin*. Dr. Ballard's commute into the depths would take 2 ½ hours. After exploring for up to four hours, he would make the arduous journey back. In those few hours each day at the bottom of the ocean, Dr. Ballard and his team were the first to witness new life forms—ones that did not need light anywhere in the ecosystem to survive. He also found the proof of sea-floor spreading along the mid-Atlantic ridge. These were amazing discoveries. Even so, putting a person on the bottom of the ocean required a tremendous effort—not only were time and money at stake, but the safety of the crew was also at risk.

Dr. Ballard kept thinking that if he could teleport himself to the bottom of the ocean he could explore so much more. Then he started thinking about robots. If a robot explored the ocean and he could see through the robot's eyes, imagine how much exploration could take place. "At first, I thought the only way to appreciate the underwater world was to physically descend beneath the waves and see it firsthand. But few people have this opportunity and even for those who can, the journey is long, frustrating, and very expensive for what time you can spend there."

He then decided to put his efforts into a robot that would explore for him.

The History of ROVs

A Remotely Operated Vehicle (ROV) is a robotic underwater vehicle that is connected to a surface ship. On board the ship, a person controls the movement of the ROV through a communications cable, often called a tether. Some ROVs carry a power source, while others receive power through a cable.

In the 1950s, the British military used ROVs to retrieve expensive practice torpedoes, and in the 1960s the United States developed ROVs to help locate and recover lost military equipment. Into the 1970s and early 80s, oil and gas companies pioneered the use of ROVs for finding new sources of petroleum that were beyond a diver's ability to reach.

At this time, ROV technology was starting to get better and cheaper, making ROVs accessible to those in the scientific community. This is when Dr. Ballard decided to push the boundaries of both research and engineering. He wrote an article for *National Geographic* Magazine that heralded a new era in underwater exploration. The article described how underwater exploration could be done from anywhere in the world with a robot.

Dr. Ballard's first search robot, *Argo*, was completed in 1985. He also sent another ROV called *JASON*, to explore the depth of the ocean. Bob used the ROVs to find the *Bismarck*, a German battleship, the *Titanic*, and *PT-109*, John F. Kennedy's ship in World War II.

Today, ROVs and closely related untethered vehicles like rovers, Autonomous Underwater Vehicles (AUVs), and Unmanned Arial Vehicles (UAVs), are making discoveries all over Earth and even on other planets like Mars.

CuteHappyBrute/flickr

How Things Work

ROVs come in all shapes and sizes designed for their tasks. Whether called an ROV, a rover, an AUV, or an AUS, these machines are designed and programmed for the environment they will explore. Whether exploring the depths of the ocean, a planet in our solar system, or the inner workings of a hurricane, the vehicles are engineering wonders. Some ROVs are operated with controls much like those found in a video game, whereas other ROVs are more autonomous (self-controlling).

ROVs have many things in common, including propulsion and navigation systems, communication systems, sensing devices, and collection and sampling tools.

Sensing Devices

Hercules is designed to study and recover artifacts from ancient shipwrecks, but it can also be used for biological and geological studies. *Hercules* has an array of cameras including High Definition and still cameras, which are used to accurately measure distance and depth and to create "mosaics." Physical oceanography sensors measure pressure, water temperature, oxygen concentration, and salinity.

Sampling Tools

Hercules has a pair of manipulator arms attached to its front end to allow it to collect samples to bring back to the surface.

Propulsion

Hercules must be able to move in any direction: forward and backward, up and down, left and right. Six hydraulic thrusters (propellers mounted within tubes) within the frame allow pinpoint control and navigation. If propulsion is lost, the ROV's slightly positive buoyancy will allow it to return to the surface.

Hercules

NOAA

Communication

Hercules uses a fiber optic cable to transmit images and data to the surface.

Try This!

Researchers like Dr. Ballard use ROVs to explore in places that are often unreachable by other means. ROVs can be controlled through radio signals or through a cable, but all rely on operators and programmers to tell the vehicle what to do. Try this challenge and experience what it is like to operate an ROV.

Materials
- R/C car
- wood blocks
- digital camera

1. Your teacher will design and set up a small obstacle course of wood blocks at one end of a room, and then place the R/C car at a starting point on the course.
2. In teams of three, assign the following roles: remote control operator, camera operator, and communicator. The remote control operator should stand as far away from the course as possible, and stand with his or her back to the course. The camera operator can stand facing the course only. The communicator can talk with both operators and bring the camera from one to another. As a team, determine how the R/C car will be controlled to successfully navigate the course. Your teacher will tell you how much time is allowed.
3. Start with the camera operator taking photos of the course and the starting location of the car.
4. Once the photos are taken, the camera operator will hand the camera to the communicator to give to the control operator, who will navigate the car through the course, using only the photos for reference. The control operator may not tell the remote control operator anything about the course.
5. The team may repeat the process of photo taking and navigation until time expires or the course is successfully navigated.
6. Try the course at least three times and see if your time to navigate the course improves.

Each team should research different ROVs and the navigation challenges they face in the environments they explore. Report your findings to your class or teacher.

ÑÄĵŵÅ/flickr

ROVs in Action

Whether called an ROV, UAV, or AUV, ROVs are used in many locations to perform a variety of tasks that are too dangerous, time-consuming, or challenging for a human to do. Whether under water, in space, or in a volcano, these vehicles are engineered to meet the wide range of challenges they face. The only limitations scientists see are getting the ROV to the location and maintaining the ROV's function in the local environment. Launched from ships, trucks, and rockets, these ROVs are expanding our knowledge of our planet and our solar system.

Peter Haydock/The JASON Project

NOAA AUV (Autonomous Underwater Vehicle)

This vehicle is pre-programmed with a route to collect ocean data like water temperature, salinity, and currents. It can stay underwater for weeks then surface to transmit the data it collected. Designed to be part of a fleet of AUVs that will help monitor the world's oceans, this AUV has crossed the Atlantic successfully.

Great Lakes Water Institute ROV (Remotely Operated Vehicle)

This ROV was instrumental in discovering invasive species—the Quagga and Zebra mussels—in Lake Michigan. Amazingly, it was assembled mostly from parts off the shelves of a local hardware store. This ROV has cameras and a vacuum-like device to collect samples from the bottom of Lake Michigan. It also has cameras to help the controller navigate the ROV to sampling locations.

Peter Haydock/The JASON Project

mynameisharsha/Flickr

Into the Future

As scientists and engineers find new uses for ROVs and other unmanned vehicles, Dr. Ballard has accepted another challenge: to help NASA find life on Europa, a moon of Jupiter. Because of the elliptical nature of its orbit, Europa is believed to have active plate tectonics. The orbit forces Europa into and out of the strong gravitational pull of Jupiter, causing the rocks deep within the moon to shift, creating friction and heat. Scientists speculate that beneath the ice on Europa's surface, lies an ocean of water which has active volcanoes. They believe the ice was melted because of this volcanic activity, creating an ocean beneath the ice. As with the search for life on Mars, many scientists think that where liquid water and volcanic activity exists, so does life.

To meet this challenge, scientists and engineers all over the world are collaborating to design a vehicle that will be launched from Earth, navigate to Europa, and land on the ice. Then the vehicle would have to deploy a ROV that would first melt its way downward through the ice, to the ocean below. At the base of the ice cover, it would release an AUV which would search for active hydrothermal vents, document what it finds, and return to its launch point to transmit the findings back to Earth through the ROV's tether. Because Dr. Ballard is a leader in ocean exploration with ROVs, he has been asked to help plan this new expedition. One can only imagine what we will find and who will be on that team of discovery.

NASA

NOAA Aerosonde UAV (Unmanned Aerial Vehicle)

This vehicle flies through hurricanes to collect weather data at lower altitudes than any manned plane can fly. Scientists are discovering that hurricanes are more complex and behave differently than can be observed by manned planes. In one case, wind speeds measured by this UAV were one full category stronger than those measured by the manned plane flying through the same storm.

Peter Haydock/The JASON Project

NASA Rover *Curiosity*

Curiosity follows in the footsteps of the Mars rovers *Spirit* and *Opportunity*. *Curiosity* is the next generation of NASA's missions to Mars. Many scientists hypothesize that where water or ice exists on Mars, so will the evidence for past or even current life. *Curiosity* is therefore designed to "follow" the water.

M. Markus/flickr

NASA's JPL

The JASON Project Argonaut Program

Join the Argonaut Adventure!

Work with and learn from the greatest explorers, scientists, and researchers in the world as they engage in today's most exciting scientific explorations. JASON is always looking for Argonauts to join our science adventure. Find out here how you can be part of the team!

Join a JASON Live Event

JASON gives you a chance to ask questions of scientists and watch them answer—live! With live demonstrations, polls, and interactivity, JASON Live Events will light the spark of inspiration in your classroom. Visit the JASON Expedition Center and click **Live Events** to learn more.

JASON researchers share their work, their inspirations, and their passion with students in JASON Live Events.

National Argonauts

Each year JASON recruits a team of expert scientists, students, and teachers to serve on our Expeditions. To learn more about the Host Researchers, log into the JASON Expedition Center to read their bios and view the Meet the Researcher videos.

Teacher Argonauts

MELINDA CARPENTER
Cowen, WV
Missions 1, 2

Melinda's inspiration to pursue science came from her 8th grade science teacher and she hopes that her experience with JASON will help inspire her students to pursue careers in science.

LISA CONSELATORE
Potomac Falls, VA
Missions 1, 2

Lisa has traveled around the world and has spent many years living abroad. She loves adventure and enjoys taking her students on outdoor adventures to inspire the spirit of curiosity and inquisitiveness in them.

MARTIN KELSEY
Liberty, MO
Missions 1, 2, 3, 4

Martin loves to incorporate technology into his classroom and to involve students. Martin believes that taking students beyond the classroom and involving them in real science is vitally important.

KELLY STEWART
Atlanta, GA
Missions 1, 2

Kelly seizes opportunities to engage students with outdoor science education. Her passion for traveling and exploring gives her unique and new ideas for getting her students excited about science.

Host Researchers

DAN SAWYER
Metrologist, National Institute of Standards and Technology, Gaithersburg, MD

Dan develops testing procedures and devices to help standardize measuring equipment, such as measuring tapes. The measuring tapes calibrated at NIST are used to test the accuracy of measuring tapes produced in the U.S. each year.

MATT BRUMBELOW
Senior Research Engineer, Insurance Institute for Highway Safety, Arlington, VA

As a student, Matt liked math and science, but didn't think he would enjoy an engineering career because it was often presented in boring ways in the classroom. Matt has found that working at IIHS is very challenging and exciting.

KOBIE BOYKINS
Staff Mechanical Engineer, NASA Jet Propulsion Lab, Pasadena, CA

Kobie worked on the first Mars rover as a college student. He is now an engineer on the latest Mars rover, *Curiosity*. He has worked on the rover's mobility system, remote sensing system, and the rover's robotic arm.

LISA JONES
Research Fish Biologist, NOAA, Biloxi, MS

As a research biologist for NOAA, Lisa frequently goes out to sea to catch fish and survey their population and life history. Lisa currently focuses on sampling and testing fish in the Gulf region for signs of oil contamination to help ensure the seafood we eat is safe.

Begin your Argonaut Adventure at *www.jason.org*

Student Argonauts

MARCELO ANCIRA
Mexico City, Monterrey, Mexico
Missions 1, 2, 4

Marcelo is an active boxer and swimmer, and is a skilled cattle roper. Marcelo loves the interdisciplinary nature of science and is particularly interested in the field of biotechnology.

MAGGY BOTROS
Wichita, KS
Missions 1, 2, 3, 4

Maggy is very involved with Girl Scouts and robotics. Maggy's passion for science led her to co-develop a local hands-on science program, designed to spark a love and enthusiasm for science in young students.

KATE BURNETT
Prosser, WA
Missions 1, 2

Kate enjoys volunteering and teaching music and ballet to young children. Kate has a natural curiosity for the world around her, which has led her to want to pursue becoming a biologist.

KENDRA ELIE
Leeds, ME
Missions 1, 2, 4

A skilled skier, musician, and writer, Kendra is truly self-motivated in all that she does. She is particularly interested in the study of the human mind.

AUBREY GONZALEZ
Harvest, AL
Missions 1, 2, 3

Aubrey loves learning about about the definitions and etymologies of unique words. She is fascinated by genetics and DNA, which has fueled her desire to study genetic diseases.

SARAH MULLINS
Pennsboro, WV
Missions 1, 2

Sarah runs track and enjoys participating in drama and volunteering at a local food pantry. Her interest in science has grown stronger over the past few years, and she particularly enjoys the science of weather.

DEAN TAYLOR
Golden, CO
Missions 1, 2

Dean's talents have led to his success as a guitar player and band performer. Dean enjoys a variety of science investigations and is particularly fascinated with atomic structure.

KARTHIK UPPALURI
Mesa, AZ
Missions 1, 2

Karthik is a competitive swimmer, participates in robotics, and plays the violin. Karthik's passion for science and interest in astronomy drive his desire to experiment and learn about the universe.

KEIANA YASUNAKA
Seaview, WA
Missions 1, 2, 3

Keiana excels at both volleyball and basketball. Computer science camp sparked her interest in technology and she continues to develop her technology and science skills through opportunities like JASON.

YOU ARE AN ARGONAUT TOO!

What are your interests? What would you want to tell other people about yourself? What do you like most about being part of the JASON community?

Interested in becoming a National Argonaut yourself and working with the next group of JASON Host Researchers? Check online often to learn about the next opportunity and how to apply!

Interact with JASON Argonauts

The **JASON Expedition Center** is your gateway to meeting the JASON National Argonauts from *Terminal Velocity*. Log into the **JASON Expedition Center**, click **Message Boards**, ask the Argos a question, and they will be happy to respond! You will also be able to discuss JASON with other students from around the world. You can also follow the Argonauts adventures through their captivating bios, journals, and photo galleries.

Students have many opportunities to get more information from the Argonauts and other experts and personal answers to their questions through the message boards and live, online events.

Photos by Peter Haydock/The JASON Project

Build a Timer

Materials
- stopwatch
- dry sand or salt
- 2 clean baby food jars of the same size (or empty soda or water bottles, any clear containers you can get clean and dried)
- scissors
- heavy paper
- hole punch
- masking tape or duct tape
- permanent marker

Assembly

1. Pour sand or salt into one baby food jar.
2. Cut a piece of heavy paper to cover the mouth of the jar. Use a hole punch to punch a hole at the center of the paper.
3. Put the paper over the mouth of the jar.
4. Place the identical jar on top of the jar with sand.
5. Using the masking or duct tape, tape the two jars together firmly.
6. Prepare your stopwatch. Turn the jars over, start the watch, and monitor as the sand falls into the lower jar.
7. When the sand has completely transferred jars, note the time on the stop watch. Record this time on your data sheet.
8. Try not to disturb your sand-clock while it is running. If your sand or salt happens to get stuck, give the jars a small tap.
9. Try this again 1-2 times and calculate the average time of the three trials.
10. Divide your timer into smaller units by dividing the total time it took the sand to move from jar-to-jar by ten and mark off the appropriate units on your jar. Use a ruler to make sure your units are divided equally. Devise a procedure to determine how long it takes sand to fill up each one of these units.
11. Verify that your units are roughly filled with sand at regular, reliable time intervals. Use the marker to mark these positions on your container. Once you are fairly confident that your intervals are regular, you are ready to move on to the next step.

In the Field

1. Use your timer in the field to take any time measurements you need, such as your classmate running around the track, or the bus moving down the street.

Build an Acceleration Detector

Materials
- soda bottle with cap (larger than 8 oz.)
- string or thread
- small metal nut
- hot glue
- water
- light corn syrup

Assembly

1. Cut a piece of string so that it hangs a bit less than three-quarters of the way down the bottle.
2. Tie the metal nut to one end of the string.
3. Attach the other end of the string to the center of the inside lid of the bottle using hot glue.
4. Fill the bottle with a mixture of 75% karo syrup and 25% water.
5. Put the lid on the bottle tightly, with the metal nut inside the bottle.
6. Shake the bottle so that the syrup and water are well mixed.

In the Field

1. Place the acceleration detector in the situation you are interested in studying, such as in a car or on the bus, and monitor the movement of the nut inside the bottle.
2. Whenever the nut moves, the bottle is undergoing acceleration. The direction of the acceleration is in the opposite direction that the nut moves.

Glossary

―――――――――――――――A―――――――――――――――

absolute zero the complete absence of thermal energy; temperature at which matter stops moving

acceleration the rate at which an object's velocity changes (a = Δv/Δt); measured in m/s² or km/h²

accuracy degree of closeness of a measured quantity to its true value

action-reaction pair forces of equal strength but opposite direction acting on two different bodies

amount of substance the number of atoms and molecules in a sample of material

ampere SI base unit for measuring electric current

Archimedes (ca 287 B.C.–ca 212 B.C.) ancient Greek mathematician known for his theories of mechanics

Archimedes's principle states that the buoyant force on an object is equal to the weight of the fluid displaced by the object

area the space inside a two-dimensional object; area = length × width; SI unit is m²

Aristotle a Greek philosopher (384 B.C.–322 B.C.) who had ideas about motion similar to Einstein

average speed the total distance traveled by the elapsed time (average speed = total distance/total time)

aerodynamics the study of the net forces acting on moving objects through air

―――――――――――――――B―――――――――――――――

balanced force occurs when the net force acting on an object is zero

base unit SI standard units for length (m); time (s); mass (g); electric current (A); thermodynamic temperature (K); amount of substance (mol); and luminous intensity (cd)

bar graph graph that uses vertical or horizontal bars to show the relationship between variables

Bernoulli, Daniel (1700–1782) Swiss mathematician who described the relationship between the velocity and pressure of a fluid

Bernoulli's principle describes the relationship between the velocity and pressure of a fluid; states that as the velocity of air or any other fluid increases, pressure decreases

block-and-tackle two or more pulleys, fixed and moveable, used to lift heavy loads

buoyancy an object's tendency to float

buoyant force an upward force found in fluids; equal to the weight of the fluid displaced by the submerged object

―――――――――――――――C―――――――――――――――

candela SI base unit of luminous intensity

calibrate the adjusting, or tuning, of an instrument so it takes correct measurements

Cartesian diver model that demonstrates Archimedes' principle of buoyancy

Celsius scale metric standard for temperature; temperature scale with 100 degrees separating the freezing point of water at 0 degrees and the boiling point of water at 100 degrees

centimeter standard SI unit of measurement equal to one hundredth of a meter (cm)

circle or pie graph represents the data as parts of a whole by dividing them into fractions that look like the pieces of a pie

circular motion movement of an object along a circular path or orbit

coefficient of friction a number that represents the degree of resistance of a surface

compound machine two or more simple machines combined to carry out complex work

constant speed occurs when there is no change in an object's speed

constant velocity occurs when there is no change in an object's velocity

conversion factor factor that is an equivalent in a different system; allows units to be changed without changing numerical values

Copernicus, Nicolaus 1473–1543 Polish scientist who theorized that Earth moves around the sun

cubit length of arm from elbow to fingertips; one of the earliest recorded measurements

―――――――――――――――D―――――――――――――――

deceleration negative value of acceleration; slowing down

density a measure of mass per unit volume of a substance (density = mass/volume)

derived unit a combination of SI base units

displace take the place of

displacement both the direction and the numerical difference between the final position and the initial position of an object, as well as the direction that the object traveled

distance how far apart two objects are

dynamics study of causes and changes of motion

―――――――――――――――E―――――――――――――――

Einstein, Alfred (1879–1955) German scientist who revolutionized Newton's theory of gravity with his theory of relativity: e=mc²

efficiency a measurement of how effectively the total energy of a system is transferred and transformed into useful energy; expressed as a percentage (efficiency = work output/work input x 100%)

electric current the flow of charges

energy the ability to do work

engineering branch of science that applies mathematical, technical, and scientific knowledge to invent new technology

estimate an approximate measurement of an object or event

―――――――――――――――F―――――――――――――――

first-class lever a lever that has the fulcrum between the input and output forces

fixed pulley a pulley that is attached to something that doesn't move; its purpose is to change the direction of a force

fluid a substance that does not have a definite shape and is able to flow

fluid friction a type of kinetic friction that occurs between a solid and a fluid object

force anything, such as a push or pull, that causes a change in the motion of a freely moveable object, or that causes stress in a fixed object; SI unit is newton

free-body diagram a map of all the forces acting on an object at a given time

free fall when any object falls due to gravity alone

friction a force two touching surfaces exert on each other that resists motion between them

fulcrum the support for a lever which enables the lever to turn or move up and down

—————————————— G ——————————————

g symbol for gravitational acceleration of objects in free-fall near Earth's surface; $g = 9.8$ m/s^2

G symbol for universal gravitational constant used to determine the gravitational force between two objects; 6.67×10^{11} m^3/kg-s^2

Galileo, Galilei (1564-1642) scientist who studied motion of objects; invented the telescope

gram metric system base unit of mass (g)

graph visual representation of data

gravitational acceleration the rate at which free falling objects accelerate due to gravity; 9.8 m/s^2 near Earth's surface

gravitational force force of attraction that exists between any two objects (g-force)

gravity force that attracts two objects with mass toward each other

—————————————— H ——————————————

Hawking, William Stephen British theoretical physicist known for his contributions to the fields of cosmology and quantum gravity, especially in the context of black holes.

horsepower a unit of power for machines; 1 horsepower (hp) = 746 watts

hydraulics a machine that uses the properties of fluids to increase force

—————————————— I ——————————————

inclined plane a ramp or any sloped surface; a type of simple machine

inertia an object's resistance to changes in its state of motion; tendency of a motionless object to remain motionless and of a moving object to continue moving with the same velocity

input force energy, power, or forces which make a machine work

instantaneous speed the speed of an object at any moment in time

—————————————— J ——————————————

joule SI unit of energy or work; 4.18 joules is equivalent to one calorie

—————————————— K ——————————————

Kelvin SI base unit of temperature; 0K is temperature where all motion in matter stops

Kepler, Johannes (1571–1630) German scientist who developed the three laws of planetary motion, published in 1609

kilogram SI base unit for mass

kinetic friction friction that acts on objects that are in motion

—————————————— L ——————————————

law of conservation of energy states that in a closed system, where no outside forces act, energy is neither created nor destroyed

law of conservation of momentum states that momentum is neither lost nor gained, it is transferred between objects; one of Newton's laws of forces and motion

length distance between two points; SI base unit of measurement

lever a type of simple machine that consists of a rigid bar that pivots or rotates at a fixed point

lift an upward force on a solid object moving through a fluid; lift helps keep airplanes in the air

line graph represents data using points that show the relationship between two experimental variables

linear motion motion in one dimension; motion in which velocity, acceleration, and displacement all occur along the same line

liter metric unit used to measure volume

load the object on which work is being done

luminous intensity the measure of light power coming from a source

—————————————— M ——————————————

machine a device that completes a task and makes work easier

magnitude a vector quantity that describes amount

mass the amount of matter in an object; the measure of a body's inertia; SI base unit of mass is the gram (g)

mechanical advantage a number that represents the number of times the input force is multiplied by a machine (mechanical advantage = output force/input force)

measurement using numbers to describe objects and events; ie: length, mass, volume, etc.

measurement error random or systematic errors that reduce the accuracy and/or precision of a measurement

measurement standard a benchmark used to compare other measures

measurement unit a standardized quantity used in a specific type of measurement

meter SI base unit for length

metric system base 10 system of weights and measures

metrologist scientist who studies systems of measurement

metrology study of measurement

model representation of objects or events; tools to explain the natural world

mole SI base unit of amount of substance

momentum the relationship between an object's mass and its velocity ($p = m \times v$)

motion a change in an object's position relative to a reference point

movable pulley a pulley that is attached to the object being moved; its purpose is to increase force

—————————————— N ——————————————

net force all forces acting on an object at any point in time, including their magnitude and direction

newton (N) SI unit of force; the amount of force required to accelerate a 1-kg mass at the rate of 1 m/s^2; 1 newton = 1 Kg m/s^2

Newton, Isaac (1642-1727) scientist who experimented and authored the three Laws of Motion and worked with optics and light

Newton's Laws of Motion set of rules developed by Sir Isaac Newton to explain how forces affect the motion of objects

Newton's First Law of Motion law of inertia; tendency of a motionless object to remain motionless and of a moving object to continue moving with the same velocity

Newton's Second Law of Motion measures the net force of an object as a direct relationship between the object's mass and its acceleration ($F = m \times a$)

Newton's Third Law of Motion states that for every action force there is an equal yet opposite reaction force

non-linear motion motion in which velocity, acceleration, and displacement do not all occur in a straight line; circular or projectile motion

—————————————— O ——————————————

orbit curved path of a satellite revolving around an object

output force energy, power, or forces provided by a machine

_____ P _____

pascal SI unit of pressure; 1 pascal (Pa) = 1 N/m^2

pascal's principle states that a change in pressure applied to an enclosed fluid at any point causes an equal change in pressure at every other point of the fluid and the container

physicist scientist who studies the interaction and structure of matter

physics/physical science the study of matter and its motion

pictograph uses picture or symbols to represent data

pie graph see circle or pie graph

power the rate at which work is performed (power = work/time); measured in SI unit watts

precision how close measurements are to each other

pressure the amount of force exerted on a specific area (pressure = force/area); measured in N/m^2

projectile any object thrown on the surface of Earth

projectile motion The path of an object that is thrown or launched horizontally and is then affected only by gravity

pulley simple machine that consists of a cable or rope running through a grooved wheel

_____ R _____

random measurement error error caused by unknown and unpredictable changes in an experiment, resulting in poor precision

rate amount of change in a measurement over a specific amount of time

reference point a fixed point or object against which motion is measured

rocket a vehicle which obtains thrust by ejecting exhaust from an engine

rocketry study of liquid or solid fuel burning engines

rolling friction a type of kinetic friction that occurs when an object, such as a wheel or a ball, rolls across a surface

_____ S _____

satellite an object that orbits another, larger object

scalar quantity quantity that has magnitude only

scientific law rule that explains a pattern in nature

scientific prefixes prefixes used to represent sets of zeros in a number

screw a simple machine that turns rotating motion into linear motion

second SI base unit of time

second-class lever a lever that has the output force between the input force and the fulcrum

SI unit International System of Units; includes seven base units: length–meter (m); mass–kilogram (kg); time–second (s); electric current–ampere (A); thermodynamic temperature–kelvin (K); amount of substance–mole (mol); luminous intensity–candela (cd)

significant digits describe how precise a number is

simple machine a device that does work with only one movement

sliding friction a type of kinetic friction that occurs when two objects slide past each other

slope steepness of the line on a graph, indicating changes in one variable in relation to another; calculated by dividing the rise by the run

speed how fast an object is moving; measured by dividing the distance travelled by the time (s = d/t)

spring scale an instrument (device) used to measure force

standard a benchmark used to compare other measures

static friction friction that opposes the movement of a stationary object

system set of components and processes related by energy transfers and transformations

systematic error experimenter errors in handling of an instrument resulting in poor accuracy

_____ T _____

technology applied science for human advancement

temperature the amount of energy within a sample of matter

terminal velocity state in which a falling object no longer accelerates

third-class lever a lever that has the input force between the output force and the fulcrum

thrust a force that pushes aircraft through the air

time a measurement of the interval between two events; SI base unit of measurement

trajectory a projectile's characteristic, arc-shaped path

_____ U _____

unbalanced force unequal forces resulting in a change in movement of an object

_____ V _____

vector arrow an arrow used to represent the magnitude and direction of a force

vector quantity quantity that describes both magnitude and direction of an object

velocity a vector quantity which represents both the speed and direction an object is moving

volume a measure of the amount of space inside an object; metric system base unit is the liter (L)

_____ W _____

watt (W) SI unit of power measurement; 1 watt is equal to 1 joule per second (J/s)

Watt, James Scottish scientists who multiplied the work capacity of the steam engine; known as father of the Industrial Revolution

wedge a double inclined plane that moves and does work; a type of simple machine

weight force of Earth's gravity on an object

wheel-and-axle a simple machine that consists of two circular of cylindrical objects fastened together and moving around a common axis

work energy used to move an object a certain distance using a force (w = f × d); measured in SI unit joules

work input the work that is put into a machine; includes the amount of force and the distance over which it is exerted

work output the work that is done by a machine; includes the amount of force and the distance over which it is exerted

Credits

The JASON Project would like to acknowledge the many people who have made valuable contributions in the development of the *Terminal Velocity* curriculum.

Partners

National Geographic Society

National Aeronautics and Space Administration (NASA)

National Oceanic and Atmospheric Administration (NOAA)

Sea Research Foundation, Inc.

Cal Ripken, Sr. Foundation

National Institute of Standards and Technology (NIST)

Insurance Institute for Highway Safety (IIHS)

NASA's Jet Propulsion Laboratory (JPL)

Host Researchers

Matt Brumbelow, Senior Research Engineer, Insurance Institute for Highway Safety, Ruckersville, VA

Dan Sawyer, Mechanical Engineer, National Institute of Standards and Technology, Gaithersburg, MD

Kobie Boykins, Mechanical Engineer, NASA's Jet Propulsion Laboratory, Pasadena, CA

Lisa Jones, Marine Fisheries Biologist, NOAA, Pascagoula, MS

Teacher Argonauts

Lisa Conselatore, Fairfax County, VA

Marty Kelsey, Liberty, MO

Kelly Stewart, Atlanta, GA

Melinda Woods-Carpenter, Summersville, WV

Student Argonauts

Marcelo Ancira, Monterrey, Mexico

Maggy Botros, Wichita, KS

Kate Burnett, Prosser, WA

Kendra Elie, Leeds, ME

Aubrey Gonzalez, Harvest, AL

Sarah Mullins, Pennsboro, WV

Dean Taylor, Golden, CO

Karthik Uppaluri, Mesa, AZ

Keiana Yasunaka, Seaview, WA

JASON Volunteer Corps

Kim Castagna, Executive Committee Chair

Mary Cahill, Executive Committee Co-Chair

Krystyna Plut, Participation and Review Committee Chair

Dee McLellan, Participation and Review Committee Co-Chair

Marjorie Sparks, Recognition Committee Chair

Marti Dekker, Communication and Membership Committee Chair

Karen Bejin, Communication and Membership Committee Co-Chair

Special Thanks

Glynn Robbins, Graphic Designer

Cassandra Love

Ron Harrison

Josh Morin

Shelley Pine

Betsy Stefany

NASA Stennis

NOAA Office of Education

NOAA - National Buoy Data Center

NOAA - National Marine Fisheries Service

United States Coast Guard

Lt Suzanne Kerver, USCG

Ensign Van Helker, NOAA R/V Gordon Gunter

Pini Kalnite, IIHS

Mark Esser, NIST

Mark Petrovich, JPL

David Seidel, JPL

U.S. Rep. Alan B. Mollohan

US Tigers Taekwondo, Gainesville, VA

Lab Field Testers

Bull Run Middle School, Gainesville, VA
- Jill Warner
- Tamara Ingalls
- Jackie Navarro

P.B. Smith Elementary, Warrenton, VA
- Barbara Dennee

Southeastern Alternative School, Midland, VA
- David Benson
- Ron Johnson
- Michael Rigo
- Randy Jones
- Brandon Seely
- Tommy Black
- Marcus Tyler

The JASON Project Board of Trustees

Dr. Robert D. Ballard, Founder and Chairman, The JASON Project

Dr. Stephen M. Coan, CEO - The JASON Project and Sea Research Foundation, Inc.

John M. Fahey, President and CEO, National Geographic Society

Terry D. Garcia, Executive Vice President, Mission Programs, National Geographic Society

Jerald T. Lundquist, Director, McKinsey and Company

The JASON Project

Dr. Stephen M. Coan, CEO - The JASON Project and Sea Research Foundation, Inc.

Michael Apfeldorf, Director, Professional Development

Denise Armstrong, CFO - The JASON Project and Sea Research Foundation, Inc.

Laura Batt, Director of Programs, Immersion Learning

Grace Bosco, Office Manager and Executive Assistant

Tammy Bruley, Business Manager

Whitney Caldwell, Manager, Professional Development

UT Chanikornpradit, Senior Applications Developer

Lee Charlton, Program Specialist

Lisa Campbell Friedman, Director, Media Production

Katie Cubina, Vice President and Executive Director of Immersion Learning

Danielle Fogg, Administrative Assistant

John Gersuk, Executive Vice President, External Relations

Peter Haydock, Vice President, Curriculum, PD, and Student Programs

Ryan Kincade, Senior Applications Developer

Arun Murugesan, Senior Applications Developer

Andre Radloff, Content and PD Producer

Nora Rappaport, National Geographic Associate Producer and Editor

Thad Ruszkowski, Grants Manager

David J. Shaub, Director, Systems Engineering and Administration

Pat Shea, Vice President, Live Events

Katie Short, Project Manager, Technology

Dr. Eleanor Smalley, Executive Vice President and Chief Operating Officer

Orion Smith, Producer, Live Events

Sean Smith, Senior Vice President & Chief Technology Officer

John Stafford, Director, Application Development

Lisa M. Thayne, Director, Curriculum Development

Todd Viola, Content Management Consultant, Nautilus Live Web Producer

Donna Zdanis, Director, Human Resources

Terminal Velocity Reviewers

Ed Adams, Montrose, CO • Linda Bebb, Traverse City, MI • Paula Bennett, Nettie, WV • Brenda Cain, Fargo, ND • Kathy Coffey, Floral Park, NY • Wendy DeMers, New Orleans, LA • Leasa Kirkpatrick, Leon, KS • Jeni Kocher-Zerphy, Annapolis, MD • Samantha Lehr, Wichita, KS • Jean May-Brett, Baton Rouge, LA • Jaun José Moreno Moguel, Monterrey, Mexico • Andrea Orvos, Amherst County, VA • Marie Papaleo, River Edge, NJ • Karen Parlett, WV • Colleen Pendergast, Binghamton, NY • Kevin Pendergast, Binghamton, NY • Kim Preston, Duluth, GA • Ann Robichaux, Houma, LA • Heather Robinson, Queensland, Australia • Jean Robinson, Coeur d'Alene, ID • Patricia Songer, Westchester, OH • Christina Terrill, Hamilton, OH • Cynthia Thieringer, Long Valley, NJ • Mari Westerhausen, Chandler, AZ • Valerie Yarmesch, Independence, OH • Tasha Yates, Hico, WV